THE NEW TECHNOLOGY

Contents

INFORMATION REVOLUTION

Lynn Myring and Ian Graham

Designed by **Roger Boffey and Iain Ashman**
Consultant editor: **Robin Mudge**

**Illustrated by Simon Roulstone, Chris Lyon,
Martin Newton, Jeremy Gower, Mick Gillah, Janos Marffy,
Mike Saunders, Roger Boffey**

Contents

About the information revolution

Many of the things you do depend upon you receiving and acting on information from other people. Catching a train, making a phone call, watching TV, buying a hamburger and going to the cinema all involve information being stored, processed and communicated. At the moment most information is stored on paper – as books, magazines, newspapers, timetables and so on. You may not be aware of it but methods of dealing with information are being revolutionized by microelectronics and computers. Computers can store vast amounts of information, not just words but pictures and sounds too. They can also process it millions of times faster than people can. You probably use computers every day without even realising it. In the supermarket your bill may be added up and printed out by a

computer terminal disguised as an ordinary cash register. The money you use to pay for the shopping may have come out of a different computer terminal at a bank. Even your voice can be electronically processed so that it travels as tiny flashes of laser light through a fibre optic telephone network, without you noticing any difference in your phone calls. Many of these things, which you will find out more about in this book, are known as information technology, or IT for short.

Information technology is not always obvious from the surface. Recent developments in microelectronics have made it possible to fit tiny "computers on a

chip" and memory chips inside everyday machines such as cars, TVs, phones and even washing machines. These are programmed to make such familiar objects

more efficient and versatile, able to process the information you put in and act on it. The supermarket cash register, for example, may be recording how much of what has been sold and working out what to order, as well as dealing with your bill.

Processing information is important but it is only part of the story. Communication is an equally vital part of the information revolution. The phone, radio and TV have all revolutionized communications between people. Information technology is providing communication between machines and people and also directly between machines. The supermarket cash register may be communicating over the phone line with another computer at a

warehouse and ordering stock that the shop needs. With IT, you too can communicate with distant computers. You can use them to shop, bank and work from home, search electronic libraries and information services on computer, get programs for your home computer and play electronic games with other people over the phone. In fact all these things are possible now and already available in some places. They will become more widespread as the information revolution advances.

3

Information technology is gradually bringing changes to all areas of life – home, work, entertainment, even everyday chores like shopping. It is providing extra ways of doing things, rather than just replacing old ones. People still write letters and read newspapers today, although the phone and TV exist. The information revolution gives another alternative; that of sending electronically prepared text and pictures by cables, like phone lines.

Most of these information technology alternatives depend upon good, two-way telecommunications links, able to carry computer data, TV channels, graphics, phone calls, text, video pictures and any other information that people want to transmit. Some links are already provided by ordinary phone and cable TV networks. As the information revolution spreads, better telecommunication networks that are specially designed for communications between the new technology machines will be set up. These will use the latest developments, such as fibre optics, lasers, microelectronics and computer control to bring about the "cabled city" of the future and the things it offers, described here.

Electronic mail: This is text, written or typed, which reaches you via cable. It can be displayed on a TV screen or printed out by an electronic printer that is permanently wired into the cable network like a phone.

Electronic publishing: Newspapers, magazines, books, in fact any kind of printed material can reach you by cable. You could call up whatever you wanted, look at it on a TV and get copies made by your colour facsimile machine of the parts you want to keep.

Teleshopping and telebanking: With a two-way cable link you can order things from shops, communicating directly with the shop's stock control computer – and pay for them by instructing your bank's computer to transfer the money. You still have to wait for delivery though.

Videotex: This is a computerized information service which reaches you by phone or TV. You can use it to look up pages of useful information. Libraries of electronic information are known as databases and getting information out of them is called accessing.

Home: The information revolution will bring more electronic equipment into use at home. The whole lot could be under the control of a central home computer that you could reach over the phone when you are out. You could instruct it to turn on lights and heating, record a TV programme onto video tape, heat your dinner, take and send phone messages, get a print of an electronic newspaper and so on.

Work: With good telecommunications an office, factory or school does not have to be in one place. Computers and the people using them can communicate as easily over long distances as in one large building. In the cabled city, teachers can mark their pupils' work, engineers can control robots in automated factories, doctors can question patients, travel agents can book holidays, bankers can monitor customers' overdrafts, and so on, all working from home and using databases of information that needs to be shared.

Entertainment: The information revolution will bring more TV channels, not only broadcast as they are now but also by satellite and cable. There will be specialist channels concentrating on different areas and even more material recorded on video tapes and discs. Computer software will also reach you by cable and there could be mass games played by thousands of people over the phone. New technology is improving ways of recording and playing music. Many films, like *Tron*, could not have been made without computers.

The new technology

The information revolution is bringing new machines into common use and changing the ways that familiar ones work and how you use them. Only a few years ago pocket calculators were expensive and much larger than they are now. Today they are small, slim, cheap and can do much more than just arithmetic – some tell the time, play tunes, work out biorhythms, tell fortunes and can be programmed. Cassette recorders have been given a new use as data storage systems for home computers – themselves almost unheard of a few years ago. These changes are being brought about by microelectronics, especially the silicon chip*, which makes machines more efficient, reliable and able to do more things.

New technology at work

This picture shows some of the new technology at work. The TV is showing a weather map of Europe made up from information from a weather satellite and sent out by videotex. The printer is wired into the phone network and is receiving electronic mail typed on a home computer keyboard, like the one shown here. With the addition of a device called a modem (see page 19) any computer can be turned into a communications terminal. The cassette machine is used for storing computer data and can contain a program to control the micro-robot. The video disc player has an interactive disc all about bicycle maintenance on the turntable and the telephone is programmed to pass any in-coming calls to another number.

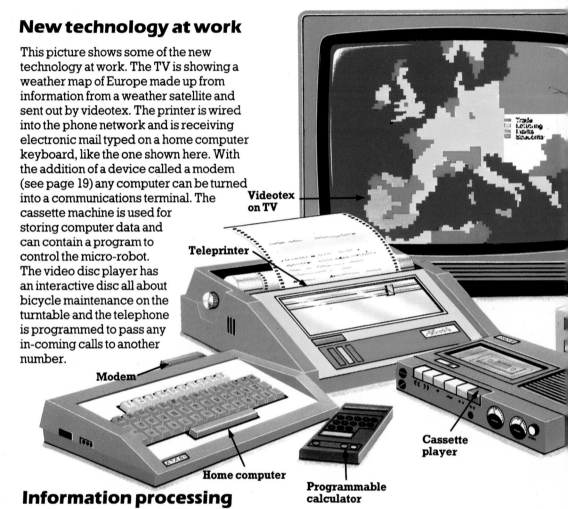

Videotex on TV

Teleprinter

Modem

Home computer

Programmable calculator

Cassette player

Information processing

Most information reaches you as words and pictures simply because this is the best way for you to understand it. Microelectronic machines deal with information in the form of electrical pulses. Any sort of information – written and spoken words, pictures, measurements, sounds, even smells – can be turned into electrical pulses and "understood" by a microchip. Information is already often stored and transmitted electronically. It then has to be processed by a machine into a form that people can understand; TV broadcasts or cassette tapes for example.

Computers are particularly good at processing information and do it so fast that they have given us new ways of looking at it. The way that computers store and retrieve information is revolutionary too. A computer can look up the electronic

6

*See page 42 for more about chips.

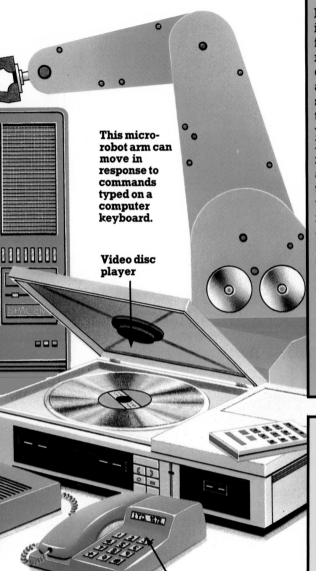

This micro-robot arm can move in response to commands typed on a computer keyboard.

Video disc player

Telephone

Driving with new technology

Driving a car is a complex task which involves processing a lot of information from many sources – what is the best route to take, how to run the engine efficiently, should you turn the wipers and lights on, what speed can you go and so on. New technology can help with all these and more. To find the best route you could load a video map of the area, key in the place you want to go, tune the radio to pick up data on traffic conditions and then follow the arrows displayed on the screen by the dashboard computer, which is programmed to use all this information. It will also automatically control the motor, lights, wipers, speed, heaters and even things impossible to change now, like the suspension and aerodynamics. Speech synthesizer chips will remind you to fasten your seat belt or drive slower and even tell you when there is a fault and how to mend it. All of these features have been tested experimentally and some are even available now.

Intelligent machines

Machines that are controlled by microchips are sometimes referred to as "smart" or "intelligent". This is because they seem to be responding to information in a clever way; doing different things in different situations. In fact, they are just following a set of instructions, called a program, electronically stored in a memory chip. The program says "If this happens . . . do that." A camera, for example, may contain a program that tells it how to work out the correct exposure for the light level and film speed. It automatically responds to information coming from the light meter by adjusting the length of time that the shutter stays open. New technology machines are often much easier to use than the non-microchip kind.

equivalent of a whole library of books in a split second. This processing speed and fast access to information means that computers can calculate things that would be impossible for people to work out because it would take too long. Space travel, for example, would be impossible without computers. Even everyday things like driving a car can be greatly improved by microelectronics, as explained above.

How computers handle information

Computers work using a very simple code made up of pulses of electricity. There are just two signals in this code – on and off – which are written down as 1s and 0s. This computer code is called a binary digital code; binary because it uses two signals and digital because it is a kind of number system.

When processed by computer all information, whatever its form, is converted into binary digital code. Pictures, text, sounds, measurements, in fact everything is turned into a stream of 1s and 0s. Information in this computerized state is known as digital information. (The word "information" is often replaced with data.) Non-digital information is called analogue. You can see the difference between analogue and digital information by comparing an ordinary watch with a digital one. The ordinary watch shows the time by constantly and smoothly moving the hands round the dial – an analogue measurement. The digital watch shows the time in numbers that change in steps, say once every second.

Bits and bytes

This telecommunications satellite is sending digital phone calls and computer data from one side of Earth to the other.

Each on and off pulse of computer code is known as a bit, short for binary digit. Most computers and other microelectronic machines use groups of eight bits to represent pieces of information, such as a letter of the alphabet, number and so on. A group of eight bits is called a byte.

Inside the computer the bits are represented by electricity, a high voltage for a 1 and a low voltage for a 0. Any sort of information can be converted into bytes if it is first turned into a stream of electricity. Lots of information reaches you as analogue electricity already – your voice is turned into electricity by a phone, music is turned into electricity when recorded and TVs make pictures from electricity. The advantage of having information as a digital code rather than a stream of analogue electricity is that it can then be directly processed by computer. This is the key to the information revolution.

What does digital information look like?

Digital information does not have to be a code of pulses of electricity. Just as it can be written down as 1s and 0s, it can also be represented in other ways. These pictures show some of them. The satellite above is beaming digital information through space.

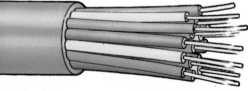

▲ The digital code can be pulses of light. This picture shows a fibre optic cable which transmits digital data as flashes of laser light.

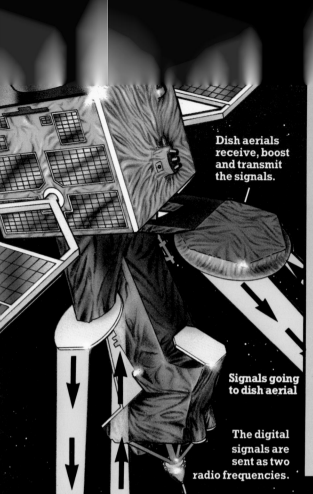

Dish aerials
receive, boost
and transmit
the signals.

Signals going
to dish aerial

The digital
signals are
sent as two
radio frequencies.

Processing digital information

Digital data has several advantages over ordinary information. Text stored electronically on floppy disk, for example, takes up much less room than the paper necessary for the same information. The main advantage, though, is that digital data can be handled by computers and other microprocessor-based new technology. Electronically stored information can be called up and easily changed using a computer. It can also be sent over the phone to another computerized machine, such as a printer.

Existing technologies are adopting digital techniques too. Digitally recorded music sounds better than ordinary recordings as it can cope better with the highest and lowest notes. Digital compact audio discs never wear out either, as they are played by a laser beam that does not touch the surface.

▼ The first computers were given digital information coded on strips of paper or cards. The 1s are represented by the holes, the 0s by the no-holes.

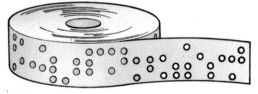

▼ Compact audio discs use a similar system for recording sounds. There are microscopic pits and no-pits in the reflective surface of the discs, which are read by a laser beam.

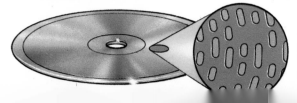

▲ Bar codes use black and white stripes to reflect a digital code of light/no light. This can be used to represent any kind of information, from music to computer programs.

▲ Digital information can be transmitted as two tones of sound – high and low. These can travel over the phone like any other kinds of sound.

Computer shopping

Computers already play an important part in shopping. Big shops, especially chain stores with branches all over the country, have to deal with very large amounts of information. They have to keep enough goods on the shelves for customers to buy, re-order stock that is low, decide which things are selling well, make sure that the price is right and so on. Computers are particularly good at monitoring this sort of flow of information. An automated system like the one shown here can keep up to date on sales and stock figures, help work out prices and even be programmed to re-order goods itself.

Stock control

When goods are delivered to the shop this information is put into the shop's computer. It then knows how much of what is in stock. As goods are sold the cash register terminals pass on this data to the computer. The computer is programmed to compare these two

This picture shows some shopping being checked out at a supermarket till. The cash register is not only a till for holding money but also a computer terminal, linked to other terminals in the shop and the main stock control computers at head office.

Bar codes

Lots of goods in the shops are now printed with a pattern of black and white stripes called a bar code. Bar codes are a way of storing digital information that can be fed straight into a computer. The black and white lines represent 1s and 0s and can be read by light. When a beam of light is passed over the bar code only the white stripes reflect back any light. This is picked up by a photodetector, which produces a pulse of electricity when it receives light. So the black and white bar code is translated into on/off pulses of electricity. The information encoded as a bar code is actually a 13 digit number. Each product has its own, unique number which tells the computer all about it.

Blogg's beans bar code

This picture shows the imaginary bar code for a tin of Blogg's baked beans. Part of the bar code tells the computer that it is a Blogg's product and all Blogg's goods will have these digits. Other digits pass on the information that it is baked beans – all makes of baked beans will include these. The rest of the digits give information about the size of the tin. The price is not included as part of the bar code as this may change. The check-out terminal looks up the prices, which are stored in its memory.

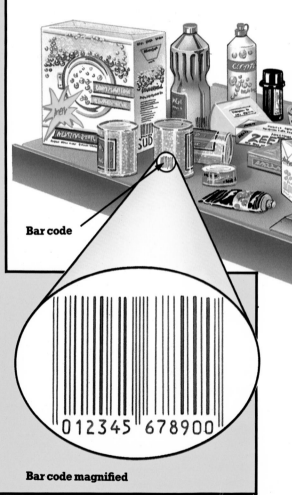

Bar code

Bar code magnified

012345 678900

figures and work out how quickly things are selling. It can then tell when to re-order different products. Stock ordering can be automated too, by programming the computer to print out the orders or even to communicate directly with manufacturers' computers over the telephone.

The cash register

This cash register has a memory containing the bar code numbers and prices of all the goods in the shop. When it gets a reading from the laser scanner it looks up the number and displays the product name and price on its display screens and prints it out as a receipt too. The cash register also records what has been sold on a tiny built-in cassette recorder. This information is used for stock control.

Usually it is necessary for only one of the cash registers to be an "intelligent" terminal with a memory. All the other cash registers are connected to it and make use of its memory to look up products and store sales information. In some systems all the cash registers are "dumb" and get their information from a computer somewhere else in the shop.

Display screens

MINTS.99

Receipt printer

Laser scanner (bar code faces down to be scanned)

Casette recorder

The shopping passes along the conveyor belt towards the laser scanner.

Laser scanner

This conveyor belt has a built-in laser scanner next to the till. A grid of beams is shone up through the clear window onto the shopping passing above. The beams read the bar codes and send on the numbers to the terminal. A grid of laser beams is used so that it doesn't matter which way round a packet is. Other systems use laser or LED (light emitting diode) wands which are passed over the bar code by the shop assistant.

11

Electronic banking

Banking is another everyday area which involves a great deal of information processing well suited to computers. Banks already use computers to keep track of customers' accounts and international money markets. They are now looking at electronic ways of replacing cash and cheques so that amounts can be transferred easily from one account to another. This is known as electronic funds transfer (EFT), or even "the cashless society". Computerized terminals are already being used for some credit card transactions.

Electronic funds transfer (EFT)

In the cashless society, plastic debit cards will take the place of cash and cheques. They are used with computerized banking terminals in shops, like the one shown below. The card is slotted into the terminal and electronically scanned. The shop assistant keys-in the price of the things that you are buying.

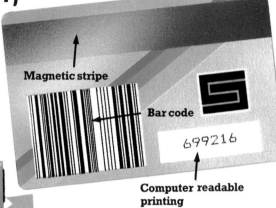

Magnetic stripe

Bar code

699216

Computer readable printing

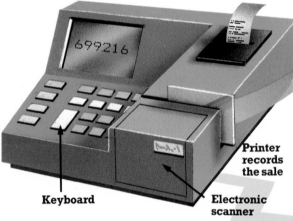

Printer records the sale

Keyboard

Electronic scanner

The debit card has your personal account number digitally encoded on the back so that it can be read directly by the terminal. The card above has the number recorded in three ways – as a magnetic stripe, a bar code and special printed characters that a computer can recognize. The terminal reads one or all of these to find out your number. (See pages 44 and 45 for how it is done.)

Some terminals just store details of debit card transactions on tape cassettes. These are later taken to the shop's bank and loaded into the main computer there for processing. The terminal pictured above, however, is an "on-line" communications machine, wired into the phone system. This means it calls the computer at the shop's bank automatically whenever a card is inserted and sends it details of the sale straight away.

    The main computer at the shop's bank calls up, by phone, the computer at the customer's bank. It tells it the account number and the amount owed, instructing it to transfer the money to the shop's account.

    Another kind of shop terminal can call up the main computer at the customer's bank to ask for payment itself, while the transaction is taking place.

PIN keypad and display screen.

When using a debit card you also have to key-in a personal identity number (PIN) on a separate keypad like the one above. This is linked to the terminal which checks your PIN against the number on the card as a security measure.

Cashpoint

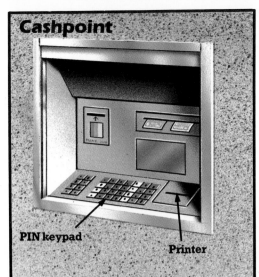

PIN keypad

Printer

The first kind of electronic bank terminals were just automatic cash dispensers. These cashpoints are linked to the bank's main computer and allow you to take out cash, order cheque books and get a statement, using a plastic card. The main computer checks your card and PIN and if all is well tells the terminal to count out the money you want. There is a printer to print out a record of the transaction. Similar terminals are also used by the staff inside the bank to give them direct access to the main computer.

Memory cards

Microchip

These EFT cards have a tiny microchip embedded within the plastic. It records the amount of money in your bank account and then subtracts what you spend while using the card. When the card is put into a terminal the chip tells it to display your balance on the PIN keypad. If the terminal is on-line to the computer at your bank, the chip can find out if anything has been paid into your account and add it to its memory. It is also programmed to add and subtract regular payments like wages and rent automatically. These cards are sometimes called "intelligent" or "smart" cards.

Home telebanking

The most convenient kind of electronic banking is done at home using viewdata.*
Your own computer is turned into a bank terminal when linked directly to your bank's computer by phone or cable TV. You can tell the bank to transfer money from your account to another, pay bills, and so on, electronically.

Transaction telephone

This telephone can make calls in the usual way, but it is also a banking terminal as it can scan and read the number on a credit card. The shop assistant uses the phone to call the computer at the credit card company and to scan the card. The phone itself passes the card number to the main computer, which checks that your account is not over its limit. If you are spending too much, the main computer automatically alerts the shop and passes the call to someone at the credit company. At the moment this is just a security check, but in the future EFT will allow the whole transaction to be automated and carried out electronically.

Credit card

13

*See page 16 for more about viewdata

TV technology

The information revolution is changing the way we use the TV – it can be a screen for home and distant computers, used for games, shopping, banking, watching films, communicating with other people and finding out information. Even ordinary TV programmes are reaching it in new ways. The TV set itself is changing too, making it more suitable for all these different functions and improving the quality of the pictures on the screen. Here are some of the developments that are taking place in TV technology.

Pocket TV

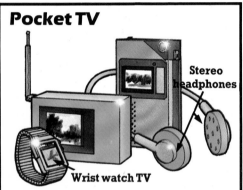

Stereo headphones

Wrist watch TV

Small, pocket TVs like those shown above are just being introduced. At the moment pocket TVs are the only ones with a flat screen. Some use liquid crystal displays (LCDs), like those used on calculators and watches. LCDs do not give a good enough picture for a large screen and only work in black and white.

Future TV

This picture shows a possible TV of the future with some of the extra things that will go with it. The set has a flat screen and is linked to hi-fi speakers for stereo sound. It is showing a cable channel that splits up the screen to show what is on the other channels. Some of the channels are interactive but the TV is also wired into the phone network to get viewdata*. This TV is also connected to a dish aerial for satellite broadcasts. There are video tape and disc players and a home computer, which use the TV's screen for display.

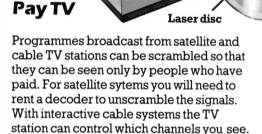

Video disc player

Laser disc

Pay TV

Programmes broadcast from satellite and cable TV stations can be scrambled so that they can be seen only by people who have paid. For satellite sytems you will need to rent a decoder to unscramble the signals. With interactive cable systems the TV station can control which channels you see.

Satellite TV

TV stations have used satellites to send each other TV programmes for many years. The signals are beamed out to space and bounced off a satellite down to another part of Earth, where they are received by a dish aerial. The receiving TV station then transmits the signals to viewers in the usual way.

The latest development is direct broadcasting by satellite, known as DBS, where the signals go straight to the viewers. You need a special dish aerial, like the one shown here, to pick up DBS TV.

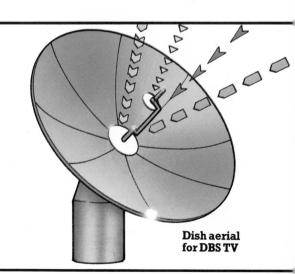

Dish aerial for DBS TV

14

*You can find out more about viewdata on the next few pages.

Digital TV

At the moment TV is not recorded or broadcast using digital techniques. This is because a vast number of bits is required to carry the information of such detailed, moving pictures. The sound part is easy to digitize and so cable and satellite TV and video discs may use digital techniques to get better sound quality and stereo. Microchips inside the TV will decode the

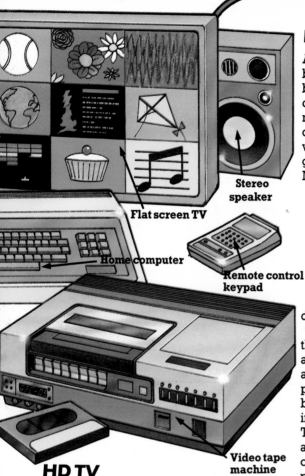

Stereo speaker

Flat screen TV

Home computer

Remote control keypad

TV control microchips

Video tape machine

digital signals and reproduce the sound.

In fact, microchips are replacing many of the electronic components in TVs. They are already used for automatic channel tuning and remote control. Chips can be pre-programmed in the factory to memorize the best possible picture and then improve the image made from the signals they pick up. The picture is stored frame by frame and any interference, wobble, ghosting, wrong colour or brightness is corrected. As the picture is electronically stored by the TV, it will be possible for you to manipulate it in various ways – split the screen to show more than one channel, zoom into part of the picture, have freeze frames, slow motion and so on.

HD TV

A TV picture is made up from hundreds of rapidly changing lines. By increasing the number of lines used it is possible to get a more detailed picture. This is called high definition (HD) TV.

Cable TV

Cable has long been used to carry ordinary TV broadcasts to places where reception is poor or in blocks of flats to reduce the number of aerials. Now specialist cable TV channels that are not broadcast in the ordinary way are also becoming common. Cable can handle many more channels than ordinary broadcasting or even DBS. This allows specialist channels, devoted to just one subject such as sport, films, news or music, to be offered. This is sometimes called "narrowcasting" as it appeals to a smaller audience.

Cable can also be interactive if there is a direct cable line between all the viewers and the TV station. This allows viewers to respond to TV programmes – perhaps take part in quiz shows, question people being interviewed or vote on issues raised.

Fibre optic cable for interactive TV

Information on your TV screen

Videotex turns your TV at home into the display screen for distant computers, giving you access to thousands of pages of useful information. You can use videotex to look-up the weather forecast, sports results, what's on at cinemas and theatres, travel timetables, get computer programs and discover facts about any number of topics.

There are two different types of videotex – viewdata and teletext. Both provide an electronic information service, but viewdata is a two-way communication system. With viewdata you can actually book a seat at the cinema or order goods, by sending a message back to the viewdata computer. This is impossible with teletext, as it is only one-way. This difference occurs because of the four ways that videotex can reach your TV, illustrated in the pictures below.

Broadcast TV: All TV signals broadcast over the air are one-way, so this method provides teletext.

Cable TV: Most cable TV channels are one-way, like ordinary TV, and so provide teletext.

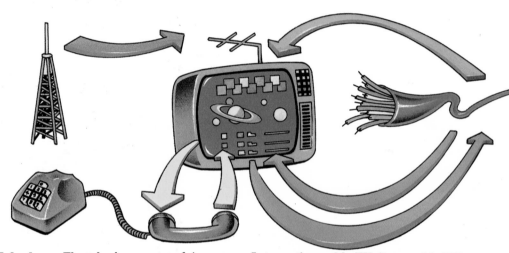

Telephone: The telephone network is a two-way communication system and so provides viewdata.

Interactive cable TV: Some cable TV systems have special channels which allow viewers to send messages back to the TV station. They provide viewdata.

Finding a page

You call up videotex pages with a special remote control keypad or keyboard provided by the videotex company, or you may be able to use your home computer in some cases. A keypad has the numbers 0 to 9 and a few symbols such as * and # and possibly some commands such as "page store". A keyboard has the letters of the alphabet as well. If you know the number of the page you want to look at, you just key-in that number. Usually you don't know the number and so go through a series of menus which offer subjects to choose

from. The menus get more and more specialized until you reach the pages with the information you want. It takes about five or six steps with viewdata, less for teletext as it has fewer pages. Some viewdata systems use a keyword search where you type in a word or phrase, such as "weather forecast", and the computer instantly finds the right pages for you. This is quicker than a menu choice, but you have to know what word or phrase to use.

Keypad

Keyboard

16

On the screen

Both viewdata and teletext provide information as screen-sized pages, sometimes called frames. The picture on the right shows part of a page in close up. Pages are made up of pictures (graphics) and writing (text) in bright colours. A page stays on the screen until you call up another, or switch off. Some adaptors have a microchip that memorizes the signals for one or more pages it has received and then displays them at your command.

How the image is made

The page is created from electronic signals sent out by the videotex computer. You have to have a special adaptor to decode these signals, so that they can be displayed on your TV screen. The image is formed on the screen by tiny squares called pixels, short for picture cells. The electronic signals tell a picture-generating chip in the decoder which pixels to light up and what colours they should be.

Graphics and text

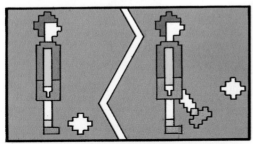

Videotex graphics and text are square and simple looking. There is no sound and the only movement possible is a simple swapping of two images, rather like a flick-picture, as shown above. The footballer looks as if he is kicking the ball because two lots of pixels are being flashed on and off alternately.

Page information

The name of the videotex service usually appears at the top of the screen with the page number and some other information. Some services show the time and date, or the name of the organization which provides the information on that page.

Viewdata

Viewdata is the more useful kind of videotex as it is interactive, which means that you can send messages back to the viewdata computer. This central computer acts as an electronic post office, storing messages and passing them on to the right people. It also controls the databases full of pages of information. You can call up and look at this information but also respond to it – to do teleshopping, telebooking, telebanking, send electronic mail and so on. Viewdata can reach you by phone or two-way cable TV. These pages show how it works and what you need to be able to get it.

Registering

The first thing that you need to do is register as a subscriber with a viewdata service. You will get a user number, like a phone number, and a pass number or word. These give you access to the viewdata computers and databases.

Viewdata is not usually free. You may have to pay a joining fee, regular charges, computer and phone charges and even a fee for some of the pages, although most are free. You will also need some extra equipment, such as an adaptor, decoding software or modem and this may be provided when you join.

The screen

One thing you must have is a TV or monitor to be your viewdata display screen. It may have to be fitted with an adaptor that turns the signals reaching the TV back into text and graphics on the screen. The adaptor contains chips programmed to decode the viewdata signals and to generate the images by lighting up the right pixels on your TV screen.

Keypad

Interactive cable TV

As cable TV systems use cables that can actually link your TV set with the TV station, it is possible to send signals both ways. You will need an adaptor for the TV to decode the viewdata signals and generate the images. Not all cable TV channels are interactive, i.e. capable of being used for two-way communications. Cable TV viewdata is very new and so not widely used yet.

Keyboards

The viewdata organization may provide a keyboard or keypad. Keyboards are better as they have the alphabet and so you can write proper messages. With a keypad you can only make choices from an index or menu, such as the one below.

Sending a greeting
choose from

1 . . . Happy birthday	3 . . . Good luck
2 . . . Valentine	4 . . . Rude message

Viewdata by phone

This is the most common way of getting viewdata. In order to use the phone for computer communications of any kind, including viewdata, you need a modem – see below for what these are. The TV and phone are linked together via the modem, or the TV is linked directly to the phone line itself.

You telephone the viewdata computer, in the usual way, and it answers your call automatically. It displays a message on the screen, asking for your user number and pass word. Having logged on to the computer by giving it this data, you can call up pages, send messages and so on. The viewdata computer monitors your call, gets the pages you ask for from the database, sends them to you and deals with all the other people using the service too.

What is a modem?

A modem is a device that converts computer data into a signal that can be sent over the phone and back again. There are several kinds of modem. One sort called an acoustic coupler is shown in the main picture on this page. The handset of your phone fits into two cups on the coupler and it converts the sounds coming out of the earpiece into electrical signals that the adaptor in the TV, or the computer, can use. It also changes the things you type into noises and feeds them into the phone's mouthpiece. Outside noises can interfere with reception when using an acoustic

This picture shows a TV and phone set up to get viewdata, using an acoustic coupler modem. There is a keypad, a keyboard and a home computer too.

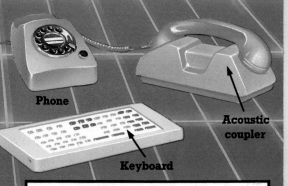

Phone

Keyboard

Acoustic coupler

Phone

Direct coupler

Viewdata and home computers

If you have a home computer you may be able to use it as a keyboard. It will also act as a decoder and image generator, so you will not need an adaptor for the TV. You will need some special software to make your computer understand the viewdata's coded signals.

coupler so that a lot of garbled letters and symbols appear on the screen.

A better kind of modem, called a direct coupler, is actually connected to the phone line. This means that it gets the phone signals as electricity from the line and you don't have to use the handset. The phone pictured above is standing on a modem of this kind. You need a special socket fitted to your phone line to plug the modem into. Some TV adaptors and computers contain modem microchips and they can also be plugged into these special sockets.

Computer

The viewdata computers and databases

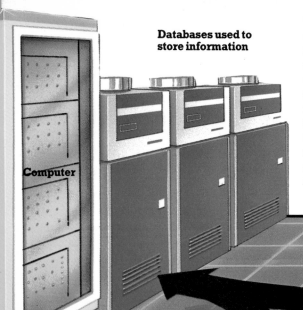

Databases used to store information

Computer

The TV and phone are the user's end of the viewdata system, but at its heart are the central computers and databases. The computers are large, powerful machines, able to organize the flow of very large amounts of information in and out of the databases. The databases are machines that hold all the pages of information, stored electronically on magnetic disks.

Information providers

The information in the databases of many general viewdata systems is not actually put together by the viewdata service. They provide the computing power, equipment and sometimes telecommunications but sell space in the databases to organization such as governments, shops, banks, airlines, newspapers, businesses – in fact anyone who wants it. These information providers (IPs) make up their pages on microcomputers like the one on the right and send them to the central database, by phone. Electronically stored information can be updated instantly, which is very useful for information that is always changing.

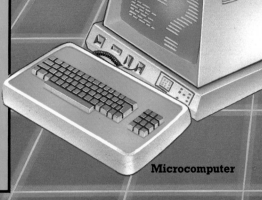

Microcomputer

Private pages

An IP can instruct the viewdata computer to allow only certain people to see some of their pages. This is called a closed user group (CUG). The computer is given the user numbers of all the people in the CUG and will then deny access to anyone else. This facility is used by companies with country-wide branches and scattered staff to provide electronic communications. Some CUGs can be joined by anyone, for a fee, and provide useful things like telesoftware computer programs.

Gateways

Lots of organizations have their own large computers and vast databases of information. These can be linked up with the viewdata network so that subscribers have direct access to them. This is sometimes called a gateway. Banks use computers a lot and with a viewdata gateway you can look up your account and instruct the computer to make payments. This is known as telebanking. You can even use viewdata to look at the arrival and departure indicator boards in an airport, if they are generated on a computer linked to the network.

1	PARIS	14	10:15
2	LONDON	17	12:55
3	NEW YORK	6	11:40
4	FRANKFURT	9	DELAYED
5		12	10:25
			10:15
			14:16

Airport indicator board

Database

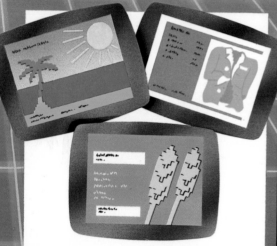

Specialist services

Not all viewdata services provide general information. Some specialize in one subject only of interest to a particular group – such as medical information for doctors, legal facts for lawyers and details of travel and holidays for travel agents.

Viewdata future

Viewdata technology and communications links could also be used for other things as well as ordinary viewdata. It could provide the basis of many of the services described in the cabled city.

If the phone line is linked by a special socket to the mains electricity of a house, it is possible for equipment to be controlled over the phone. The gas, electricity and other meters could be read over the phone by computers at the electricity or gas office.

It may also be possible to have a central, computer-controlled library of video discs that you could call up and choose from over cable TV, just like pages of videotex. Viewphones, where you see on your TV the person you are talking to on the phone, are another possibility for the future.

21

Teletext

Teletext is another kind of videotex that brings screen-sized pages of information to your TV from a central computer. Teletext is broadcast on TV channels at the same time as ordinary TV programs and picked up by your TV in the usual way. You need a special teletext adaptor to decode and display the digital teletext signals. Some TVs have a decoder already fitted, or you can buy one to adapt an old TV. You also need a remote control teletext keypad, like the one below, to call up pages you want.

As teletext is broadcast, it is a one-way only system, unlike viewdata. In fact it differs from viewdata in several ways, which are explained on these two pages.

Transmitting teletext

Teletext pages are made up and stored electronically by computers similar to those used for viewdata. Teletext services usually have fewer pages than viewdata – just a few hundred rather than thousands. The pages are broadcast one after another as a continuous stream and it takes a couple of minutes to send out the whole lot. Once they have all been broadcast the cycle starts again. This means that the pages are not all available at the same time, as on viewdata. You will have to wait for the one you want to be broadcast. This is usually only a few seconds, but it depends upon the total number of pages and whether you have just missed it. Popular pages appear more than once in a cycle. Teletext pages are numbered and you choose what you want to see from menus and call it up with the keypad.

These keys are used for controlling the teletext pages.

These keys control the TV channel selection.

A teletext keypad like this instructs the TV to switch from ordinary programmes to teletext. Most remote control keypads work by sending out instructions coded by a beam of infra-red light. An infra-red receiver in the TV set picks up and decodes these instructions and passes them on to the teletext adaptor.

The symbols control the special functions that teletext offers, which are shown on the right. A page remains unchanged on the screen once it has been displayed.

22

In Britain the BBC's teletext is called Ceefax, the ITV's is called Oracle.

Teletext signals

All TV pictures are made up of hundreds of horizontal lines which change many times a second to produce the familiar moving pictures on the screen. There are a few spare lines, which are not used for the normal TV image, at the top and bottom of the screen. The top lines are used for teletext signals, the bottom ones carry information for TV engineers at the transmitters. On a badly tuned TV, where the picture has slipped and the top spare lines show, you can see the digital code of teletext signals as a series of rapidly changing bright dots. These tell the microchips in the adaptor what to display to make a page. The microchips wait for the page you want, store the signals that form it and then display the page on the screen.

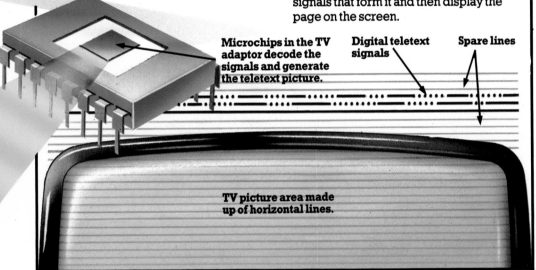

Microchips in the TV adaptor decode the signals and generate the teletext picture.

Digital teletext signals

Spare lines

TV picture area made up of horizontal lines.

What's on teletext

Like viewdata, teletext provides lots of useful information such as news, sports results, weather, recipes, travel guides, puzzles and so on. Although there is less information than on viewdata and it is not interactive, teletext does have some advantages. It is free, apart from the cost of an adaptor. Also, as the teletext is being continuously broadcast on the

!NEWS FLASH! All planes are arriving late due to fog.

same channel as TV programmes and at the same time, it has some features that viewdata does not. Teletext can be mixed with an ordinary programme to give sub-titles on the screen in time with the pictures. The adaptor can be programmed to display a certain page at a particular time, an airport's timetable when you are awaiting a plane to arrive, for example. You can also ask for a page to appear as soon as it is updated, say to get a news flash like the one above.

Telesoftware

If you have a home computer, you need programs to run on it. Telesoftware is a new, very convenient way of getting computer programs, via videotex. The software is loaded directly into your computer. It can reach you as broadcast teletext signals or as viewdata, either by interactive cable TV or phone line. Telesoftware is much easier than typing long programs from magazines and can be cheaper than buying cassettes.

Getting telesoftware

Telesoftware programs are written as pages of text, stored in the videotex company's database and transmitted just like any other kind of videotex information. Teletext telesoftware is broadcast, viewdata telesoftware is sent down the phone line or via cable TV.

You may need some extra equipment, such as an adaptor or modem, in order to pick up videotex. Some special software that enables your computer to understand the videotex code may also be necessary.

Telesoftware services often provide much more than just programs – pages of computer and software news, reviews, hints, letters, advertisements and puzzles for instance. You may have to pay for some programs and for the telesoftware service itself if it reaches you as pay TV or phone viewdata. Teletext is usually free.

Teletext telesoftware

Teletext telesoftware usually has fewer programs available than viewdata and they will probably be shorter. You need a special adaptor/receiver, which you connect to your computer, to pick up the teletext signals. This is because if you are using your TV as the display screen for your home computer, it will be tuned to the channel that the computer uses. The TV cannot receive the teletext channel at the same time, so you need another receiver to do this. The adaptor also decodes the teletext signals so you do not need a special teletext TV or extra software. Another reason for having a separate adaptor/receiver is because the TV cannot feed the teletext information into the computer.

Cable software

If the telesoftware is part of an interactive cable TV service, it is likely to be on a pay-channel that is devoted to viewdata. You must pay to see the channel, as well as for the software you want. You may need a special adaptor fitted to your TV so that it can pick up the signals and send them to your computer, as well as some software to allow your computer to decode these signals.

One day it may even be possible to use telesoftware via viewdata without even having your own computer. The central viewdata computers could run programs for you, displaying the results like ordinary pages for you to control with the teletext keypad.

This software programs your computer to decode the teletext signals.

Tapes and cassette for saving telesoftware.

Computer used to run the telesoftware

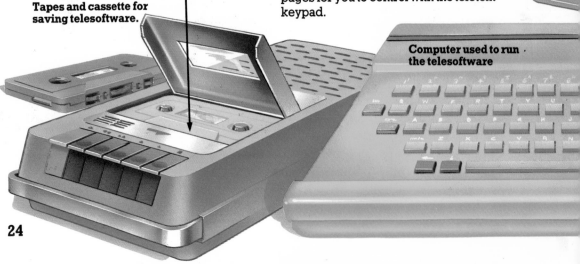

Software by phone

To get telesoftware from a phone viewdata service you need to be set up to receive viewdata, as described on pages 18 and 19. Telesoftware by phone is likely to be provided by a closed user group that has rented space in the viewdata database. Once you have joined to get telesoftware you will be able to get the other viewdata services too. The picture below shows a home computer receiving a games program over the phone, using an acoustic coupler modem.

TV used as a display screen for telesoftware

Downloading telesoftware

Putting telesoftware into your computer is called downloading. You choose programs that you want from menus. They are usually grouped by subject, such as games, business, education and so on, but even more importantly by kind of computer. This is because programs written for one computer will not run on another kind. Computer programs are written in special computer languages, usually BASIC or machine code for home computers. Unfortunately different kinds of computer use different versions of BASIC and machine code, so you will only be able to download software written for your type of computer.

While it is downloading, a program may appear on your TV screen as lines of words, letters and symbols, which often look like rubbish. This is because programs are transmitted in a special compacted code that is shorter and therefore faster to send than ordinary computer languages. Once the program is loaded you can run it, store it on tape or disk for future use, display it on the screen or print it out if you want to see it written down.

Phone and acoustic coupler modem

The electronic office

Most office work involves dealing with information written down on pieces of paper. When it is not being processed by people, this paper is filed away for future reference. This is not a particularly easy or fast way of dealing with information – a computerized system can be much more efficient. The office of the future is sometimes called "the paperless office" as all the information is stored electronically. These pages look at some of the changes that are taking place now.

Data links

✳ As all the work stations are linked together they can be used for electronic mail. You can send memos and letters to anyone else in the office, even to everyone at once.
✳ The work stations have a calender/diary for you to record all your appointments. You can arrange meetings with other people electronically, using your terminal to scan

Work stations

In the electronic office people will work at computerized work stations, like the one shown below. It is made up of a microcomputer keyboard, visual display unit (VDU) and a telephone. Several work stations may share other equipment such as printers and intelligent photocopiers. All the work stations in the office are linked together and to a central computer and database of information.

This diagram shows how several work stations can be linked together as a network. They all share a big central computer and database.

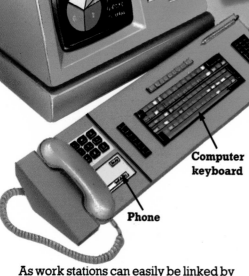

Work station

VDU screen

Disk drives

Computer keyboard

Phone

Networking

Communications are vital to the electronic office. The work stations in a single building will be linked together by cables to form a network. This enables information to be passed between people electronically, say for approval or further processing. The receiving work station can store the data or alert its user, depending upon the priority rating given to the message. A work station phone has a built-in modem so that computer data can be transmitted easily outside the office. With satellite links, a company in America can send data direct to its European office in seconds.

As work stations can easily be linked by phone it is possible for people to have their work station at home. The office of the future may be an electronic network rather than a building.

the diaries of the people you want to meet to see when they are all free.

✳ You can also send electronic voice messages over the phone. The receiving work station records your voice digitally and plays it back as a commentary to go with information on the screen.

✳ Every work station has access to the same database of information but can run its own program to deal with it in different ways.

Working with computers

As work stations are computers you can run programs which help with your work. Computers can manipulate information very fast, doing in a few seconds things that would be impossible without the help of a computer.

Word processing programs make writing and changing documents much easier (see pages 28 and 29). Other programs automatically work out things like the wages – printing out individual payslips and transferring the right amount of money for every member of staff. Modelling programs allow you to work out what would happen if various things change in different ways in relation to each other.

The electronic office also automates many of the routine jobs like re-typing standard documents and addressing mail, as computers can be programmed to control other electronic machines. Even familiar office equipment such as photocopiers and telex machines can be controlled by computer and improved by microelectronics.

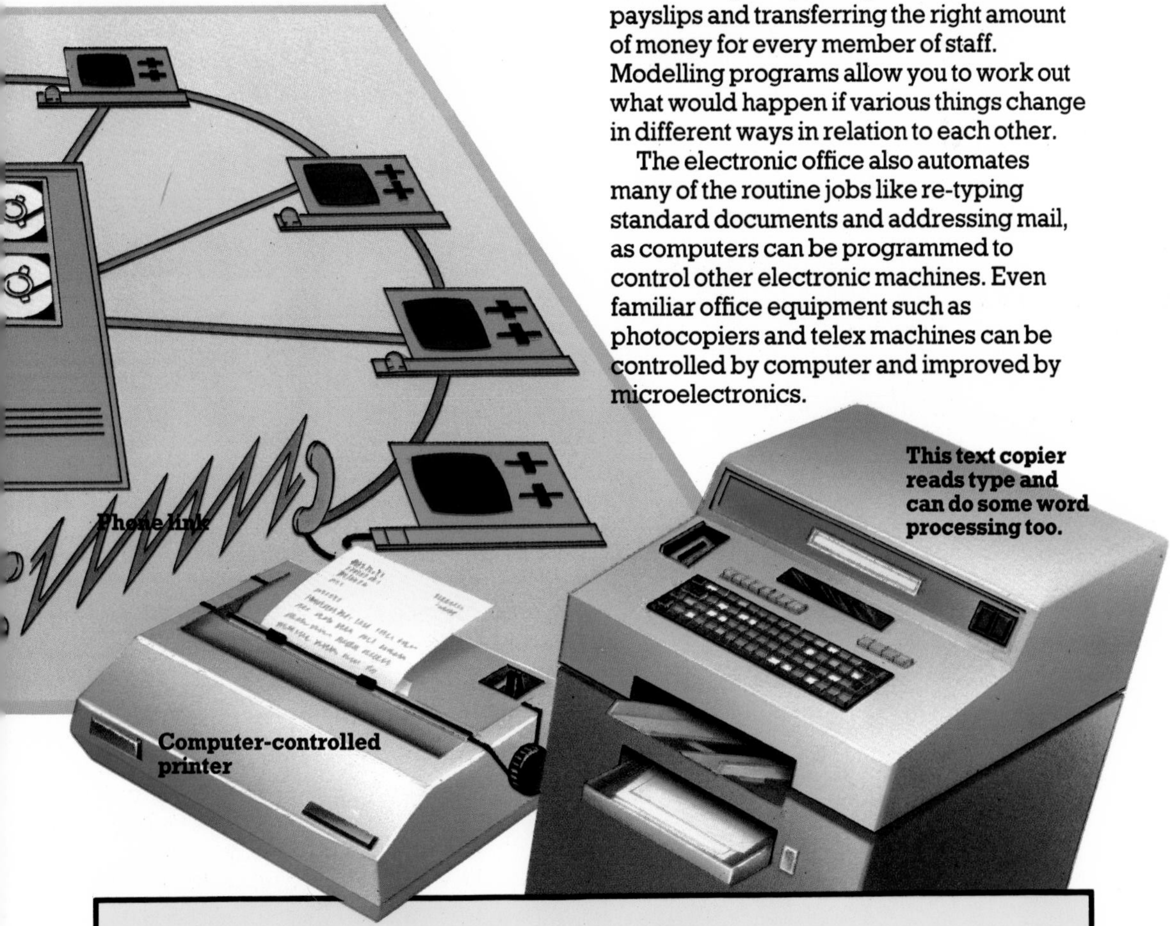

Phone line

This text copier reads type and can do some word processing too.

Computer-controlled printer

Machines that "read" and "write"

Even in the electronic office information will still need to be put on paper sometimes, so machines that can automatically read text for storage or reproduction are very useful. They save having to re-type or word process written documents if there is just a small change to be made. The picture above shows a machine that can read type and be programmed to change parts of a document before making copies of it. The other machine is a computer-controlled printer which can type a page of text in seconds.

Word processors are revolutionizing writing in the same way that electronic calculators have already affected arithmetic. They are computers designed to make the manipulation of text quick and easy. With a word processor you can electronically edit what you have written, completely changing the layout, order of words and sentences and even replace words without having to re-type the whole thing.

This picture shows a dedicated computer which cannot do anything but word processing. Dedicated machines like this have a keyboard with special keys that control the editing and other functions, to make them easier to use. You can also buy word processing programs on disk, tape or chip to run with an ordinary computer.

Using a word processor

Your text is displayed on the VDU as you type it in at the keyboard. You can make changes and corrections as you go along, using the editing keys and a movable pointer, called the cursor, to tell the word processor what to change. The text is stored inside the word processor's memory, as well as being displayed, so you can go back over it later. You can also store it permanently on disk, or tape, for reference or later editing. A word processor has to be connected to an electronic printer in order to produce a typed copy of your text stored in its memory. It takes a little time to learn to use a word processor as they can do so many things. Here are some of the main functions.

Word search

Global search is a useful command which automatically searches for and replaces a particular word, every time it occurs anywhere in the text. For example if you have just finished your 80,000 word novel "The life of Tiddles" and decide to change the hero's name to Bonzo, the word processor will look at all 80,000 words and replaces every Tiddles with Bonzo, instantly. You can also search selectively, with the word processor stopping every time it finds the word so that you can decide whether to change it.

Editing

After writing your text you will probably want to edit it, to get rid of mistakes and make changes. With an ordinary typewriter this would mean a lot of re-typing but with a word processor you can do it electronically before printing. You can remove any words and the word processor will automatically close up the space left, repositioning the rest of the paragraph too. Inserting extra words is also easy and the word processor readjusts the rest of the text to fit them in. An overwriting function lets you replace unwanted words with new ones. The word processor will also move parts of the text around if you want to change the order but not the words.

Words on a chip

Until recently, most word processors were large office machines. Now you can buy a word processing program permanently stored on a microchip to fit in your home computer. It will not do as much as an office machine but should do the things mentioned here.

Page design

You have to tell the word processor how to arrange the text that you are writing. Once you have specified the line length and spacing, indentations, margins, headings, pages and so on you are ready to type. The machine automatically lays out the text when it is printed. If a word is too long to fit on the end of a line the word processor takes it down to the next, on screen as well as when printed.

```
THE FURRY
FOUR-LEGGED
FELINE SETTLED
DOWN ON THE
LOOSE FITTING
FLOOR COVERING
```

Word processor

Disk drives

Keyboard and
editing keys.

Extra programs

THE CAT SAT ON THE MAT

Additional programs are available on disk to help you improve your writing. A spelling program compares every word in your text to the thousands of words it has stored as a dictionary on disk. If it finds a word not in the dictionary, the word processor highlights it on the screen for you to check your spelling or typing and correct any errors.

If you are stuck for a good word you can use a thesaurus program to supply synonyms (words of similar meaning) to the one you indicate. Another program will even check your grammar against rules stored on disk and suggest changes for you to insert. It is even possible to have a program to improve your English. This will suggest simpler ways of putting things if you have been too wordy, as illustrated here on the screen and picture above.

Microwriter

This is a Microwriter. It is an electronic word processor but does not have a standard keyboard. Instead you press a combination of its six keys to produce all the letters of the alphabet, numbers, symbols and to give the Microwriter special commands. Your text moves across the one line display and is stored inside the machine. You can edit and correct with a Microwriter and also link it to other electronic machines such as TVs, word processors, computers, printers, cassettes and modems for further text editing, processing, printing, storage and communications. It is rather like a "word calculator".

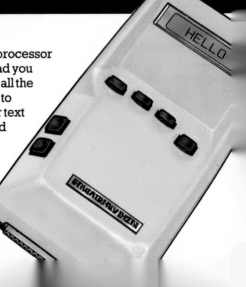

Future phones

Microelectronic technology is enabling the phone to do much more than just make and receive calls. The telephone of tomorrow will be more useful than the one you use today. In fact many of these developments are available already but are not yet very common. Here are some of the things that you can expect to find being added to your phones over the next few years.

Making connections

TV

Computer

Printer

Phones will be fitted with special sockets so that they can be connected to electronic machines, like printers, computers and TVs, that need telecommunications links. They will also have built-in modems for data transmission.

Directory enquiries

With the phone of the future you will not need a pile of thick telephone directories full of numbers that you will never want to know. Instead, all directories will be electronically stored on a computer database and you will make enquiries over the phone using a kind of viewdata. A computerized system will be much faster than an operator and will even be able to find numbers if you are not sure of the spelling of a name or just know the address.

Display screen shows numbers and messages

Command keys for programming the phone

Programmable phones

Telephones will contain microchips programmed to carry out various functions, like the ones listed here, at your command. The keyboard will have the usual numbers and some special programming keys too, possibly even an alphabetic keyboard.

Automatic calling: The phone will memorize frequently used numbers and automatically call them in response to a single digit code.

Call bar: You will be able to program your phone to stop any calls being made either to or from your phone, say while you are on holiday.

Re-routing: If you are going to be at another number you can get your phone to transfer your calls to it.

Repeat call: The phone will keep trying a number that is busy and let you know when it has got through.

Voice messages: These are digitally recorded messages. Chips will be able to play messages to people and record their messages while you are out.

Display screen

The built-in display screens will show the number that you call so that you can see if you have made a mistake and also display the cost as you are speaking, or at the end of a call. It can also show the number of a phone making an incoming call so that you can see who it is before answering . . . or not. The display will also tell you if someone is calling your number while you are on the phone or have barred in-coming calls.

Number keys

Speech synthesis

Phones will contain chips that speak to your callers when you can't. They will be ready programmed to tell someone who is trying to call you if their call is being re-routed to another phone or, that the line is busy.

Computerized phone exchanges will also use speech synthesis to give callers information, automatically. The computer will monitor a call, work out the cost and pass this data to the speech chips to say.

Radio telephones

Short range mobile phone

A phone does not have to be at the end of a cable but can work with radio waves too. In fact lots of phone calls travel as radio waves now. Some long distance and all satellite links are made by microwave – a kind of radio.

Short range cordless phones, like the one above, use an adaptor fitted to your ordinary phone. This converts the electrical waves of incoming calls into radio waves and broadcasts them to the mobile radio phone. Speaking into the radio phone produces radio waves that are picked up by the adaptor and sent down the phone line in the usual way.

Cellular systems

Short range radio phones only work with an adaptor on an ordinary phone and can cover only a small area. Completely radio networks can work over long distances and do not need a connection with the ordinary phone lines at all. They work by having an overlapping network of computer-controlled radio transmitters. Each one covers a small zone, known as a cell, and calls are routed through cells until they reach the one that the receiving phone is in. This sort of system allows phones to be mobile as the computers pass your call from one cell to another as you move around between them.

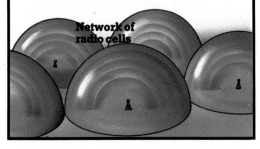

Network of radio cells

What does "telecommunications" mean?

The word telecommunications means communication over a long distance. Broadcasting TV and radio signals is one form of telecommunication, but the main two-way telecommunications system in use today is the telephone network. It was designed and set up to transmit voices so that people could speak to each other. The information revolution depends upon good communications between computers. Services such as viewdata, teleshopping, electronic banking, the electronic office and so on cannot work without good telecommunications links. Phone networks are being redeveloped to make computer communication easier.

How phones work now

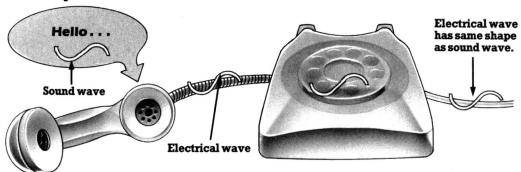

Hello . . .

Sound wave

Electrical wave

Electrical wave has same shape as sound wave.

When you speak your voice produces a sound wave in the air. This is turned into an electrical wave by a microphone inside the mouthpiece of your phone. The electrical wave representing your voice travels along cables in the phone network, through exchanges which route it in the right direction, to the receiving phone. At this phone's earpiece, the electrical wave is converted back into a sound wave, recreating your voice. This sort of system is called analogue transmission, as the electrical wave is analogous (similar) to the sound wave.

Facsimile transmission

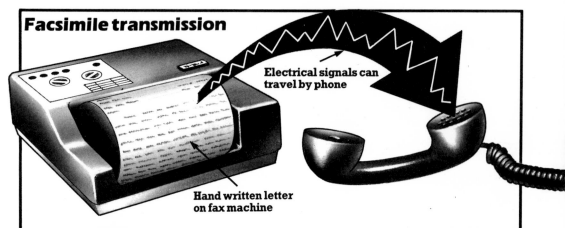

Electrical signals can travel by phone

Hand written letter on fax machine

Telephones and computers are not the only machines that can communicate by phone lines. This is a facsimile (fax) machine, which can send and receive any kind of document – printed or hand written text, painted or photographed pictures. They work by scanning the document, reading the degree of lightness and darkness all over the page. These values are converted into electrical signals that can be sent through the phone system. The receiving machine, which is called up like a phone, decodes the electrical signals and prints out a facsimile (exact copy) of the original. Other kinds of telecommunications machines with keyboards, can send and receive typed messages over the phone.

Digital phone systems

Computers work with digital signals not analogue, so when they communicate by phone their data has to be converted by a modem at both ends. Computer communication would be much easier if the phone system worked digitally and could transmit computer data without converting it. Many phone networks are being changed so that they can deal directly with digital data and some are already partly digital. In this kind of system, voices need to be "digitized" for the journey. This picture shows how it is done.

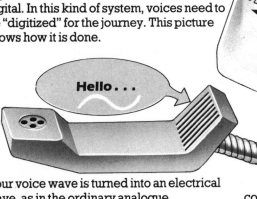

Electrical wave representing your voice is measured and turned into digital 1s and 0s.

Your voice wave is turned into an electrical wave, as in the ordinary analogue telephone system. The wave is measured thousands of times a second, giving a series of numbers which represent its height at different times. These numbers are converted into binary digital data – on/off bits – which can be transmitted as pulses through the phone system. At the other end, the bits are converted back into the sound of your voice.

Computer exchanges

Even though the phone system is not yet completely digital, exchanges which route calls through the network are being computerized. These can handle more information, more quickly than the old mechanical exchanges so there should be fewer misconnections, crossed lines, interference and lost calls. Computer-controlled exchanges can also offer extra services such as re-routing calls to another phone, viewdata phone number directories, automatic monitoring of calls and voice synthesis for passing on routine information such as the cost of calls or messages about busy lines.

Fibre optic cables

Fibre optic cable

At the moment most phone calls travel as electricity along copper cables but they can also be sent as light along thin strands of glass called optical fibres. The advantage of optical fibres is that they can carry much more information than copper cables. This picture shows a bundle of optical fibres capable of transmitting 10,000 telephone calls, compared with the copper cables necessary. Another advantage of fibre optics is that the phone line cannot be tapped.

Copper cable

33

See pages 36 and 37 for more on fibre optics.

Satellite Communications

Telecommunications messages are not only broadcast and sent along phone cables, but also beamed out into space and bounced off satellites. Every day thousands of phone calls, TV signals and streams of computer data travel from one side of the world to the other in seconds via satellites.

Communications satellites can handle more information than cables and also transmit it much faster. Computer data that would take all day to send by phone could reach its destination in just a quarter of an hour by satellite.

Sending signals

Information is beamed to and from satellites as microwave signals, which are a kind of short radio wave that can travel through space. The signals are sent and received by dish-shaped aerials called earth stations. When satellite communication was first developed, aerials had to be huge. Now

This dish aerial on the roof of the *Financial Times* building in central London was used experimentally to beam the paper to a printer in Germany.

they are small enough to be installed in a car park or on a roof, like the one shown here. America's national newspaper *USA Today* is only possible because a satellite can transmit it directly to newspaper offices all over the country where it can be printed and distributed locally.

Satellite orbits

A telecommunications satellite must be in the same place in the sky all the time, so that the earth stations can be pointed towards it. This will only happen when a satellite is 35,800km (22,300mi) above the equator. This is called a geosynchronous orbit. In this orbit a satellite takes exactly the same time to orbit the earth as the Earth takes to rotate once on its axis

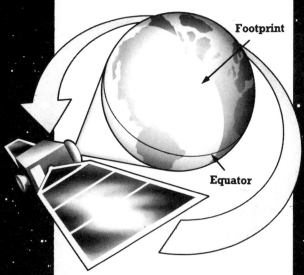

Footprint

Equator

(23hrs 56mins). The satellite is always above the same place on Earth and seems to hover motionless in the sky. One satellite can cover only about 40% of the Earth and the area that it covers is known as its footprint.

Using satellites

You will need your own small dish aerial if you want to get TV broadcast by satellite – known as DBS. Even without your own aerial you can still use communication satellites, via the ordinary phone network. You have probably sent your voice by satellite if you have ever made a very long distance phone call.

Direct satellite links could be useful for multinational organizations – all their offices round the world could be linked together, office work stations could communicate with each other, central databases be accessed by terminals on another continent, or a central computer could send new instructions to a robot thousands of kilometres away and so on.

At the satellite

The satellite picks up the signals with small dish-shaped aerials and then transmits them back to a different part of Earth. It also boosts the signals, making them easier for small aerials to receive. Signals from a satellite can be picked up by any suitable aerial in its footprint.

Information that needs to be kept secret, such as computer data, has to be coded or scrambled before transmission. An aerial can pick up signals from all the satellites whose footprints cover it.

Only the very newest satellites can handle digital data. The older ones use analogue techniques and so are slower and transmit less information. Newer satellites are bigger too and can boost the signal so much that even tiny aerials, like those used for DBS TV, can receive the signals.

Dish aerials

There are over 170 telecommunications satellites in space already and several more are planned to be launched over the next few years. Some will be dedicated to data transmission or DBS TV instead of general telecommunications. The geosynchronous orbit is getting so crowded that neighbouring satellites have to use different radio frequencies to stop interference between signals.

Picking up signals

Most satellite signals cannot be picked up by ordinary radios but only by the special dish-shaped aerials. The signals are so weak they have to be concentrated together by the dish of the aerial. The microwaves hit the inside of the dish and are all bounced to the same place, just above the middle of the dish. This is the focus point. The aerial has to be tuned, as different messages are transmitted at different frequencies, just like ordinary radio. Dishes must also be carefully positioned to get signals from particular satellites.

The aerial turns the radio signals it picks up into electricity. This is sent, by wire, to the receiving machine, which could be a TV, telephone exchange, computer or whatever, and decoded back into its original form.

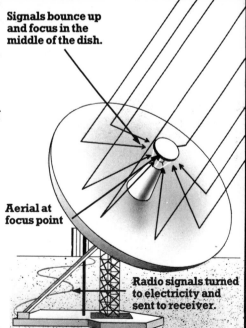

Signals bounce up and focus in the middle of the dish.

Aerial at focus point

Radio signals turned to electricity and sent to receiver.

Fibre optics

At the moment most telecommunications links for phones, cable TV, computers and so on are made with copper cables which carry messages as electricity. Optical fibres are a new kind of communications cable that use light rather than electricity. They will probably become widely used in the future as they can carry more TV channels or phone calls in a single cable than copper cables can. Optical fibres are also better suited to the two-way, interactive links needed for viewdata and other computer communications. They are already being used by telephone companies but are not yet very common, as ordinary copper cabling is usually cheaper.

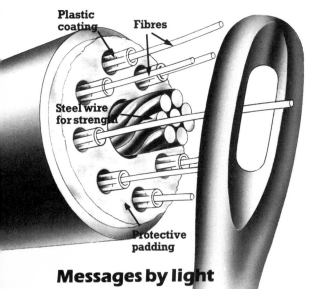

Plastic coating

Fibres

Steel wire for strength

Protective padding

Channelling light

Light was not used for telecommunications in the past as there was no way of channelling it from place to place. It cannot be broadcast like radio waves or travel along metal wires like electricity. It was the invention of optical fibres in the 1960s that provided a channel. Optical fibres are tubes of glass (or sometimes plastic), stretched as thin as hair, like the ones shown here. The fibres are completely flexible and can be bent and twisted like wire. They are used bundled together to form cables. Light can travel along a fibre in a continuous beam, or as digital on/off pulses.

Messages by light

Light is just one part of the electromagnetic spectrum, pictured below, which includes radio waves. We are used to the idea of radio waves carrying information to our TVs and radios but light can do this too. In fact it can transmit more information than radio.

| Radio waves | Micro waves | Infra-red | Visible light | Ultra-violet | X-rays | Gamma-rays |

All electromagnetic radiation takes the form of waves. The waves are measured in length – the distance between waves – and frequency – the number of waves a second. Different kinds of waves have different lengths and frequencies. The shorter the wavelength, the higher its frequency. It is rather like comparing a giant's footsteps with a dwarf's. In one second a giant can make one long step, a dwarf takes lots of little ones. Light has a very much shorter wavelength than radio. Millions of light waves can fit into a single millimetre, but a single radio wave can be thousands of metres long. This means that light has more waves a second which can be used to carry information and so can transmit a greater amount than radio can, in the same time.

This diagram is not to scale

Light waves

Radio waves

Time

36

How optical fibres work

Optical fibres are made from glass so clear and pure that a sheet 35km thick would be as transparent as an ordinary window pane. Light does not leak out of the fibres because they have an outer cladding of different glass. This makes the light bounce back into the very pure core at the centre, as illustrated here. The light travels along the fibre bouncing from side to side.

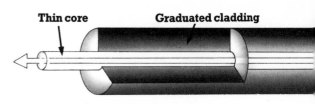

The most modern, and expensive, kind of optical fibres have a carefully graded cladding and an extremely thin core that keep the light in a straight line. These are used with lasers. the only light source to produce a parallel beam.

Light sources

As optical fibres are so thin, the light source used to flash light into them must be tiny too. Small light-emitting diodes (LEDs) or laser "chips" are used. LEDs are electronic devices which produce a light when they receive an electric current. Laser chips are made from tiny crystals of chemicals which give off pulses of laser light when excited by electricity. Laser light is not like ordinary light, but consists of just one wavelength concentrated into a straight beam.

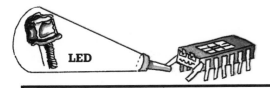

LED

Transmitting signals

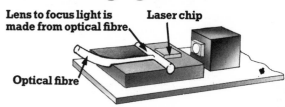

Signals transmitted by optical fibres can be analogue or digital. The message is turned into an electric current, which is used to excite the laser chip, or LED, into producing flashes of light. These light flashes have to be focused into the optical fibre by a lens which is also made from an optical fibre. The light travels along the fibre to the receiving end. Here there is a photodetector which converts the light back into an electric current. This electric current is then decoded back into its original form.

Messages in packets

With a digital transmission system, cables can carry individual messages chopped up into lots of little digital packets of about 10 bits, stacked with packets from other messages. Packets from phone calls, cable TV, computer data, viewdata and so on, can all travel together stacked in the same cable. The packets are sorted and put back together at the receiving end to form the original messages. Packets making up a single message even travel along different cables to reach the same destination at the same time. This allows the most efficient use of available cables. These techniques can be used with ordinary cables as well as optical fibres.

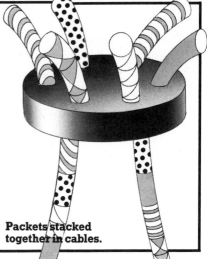

Packets stacked together in cables.

37

The revolution in factories

Office work has only recently been affected by microelectronics and computers, but other industries have been quicker to automate and use new technology. Most industries are concerned with making things, from aircraft to currant buns. Computers can operate machines and control manufacturing processes such as chemical production. Computers are also widely used to help in the initial design of products. Here are just some of the developments that have been taking place in industry.

Computer aided design (CAD)

Design is a big growth area for computers in industry. They are being used to help design things as diverse as cars and shoes. With the right sort of program a designer can make the computer simulate what will happen if a particular design is built. By changing aspects of the design, the designer can see what is likely to occur as a result. The computer saves the designer from actually building unsuitable designs, just to find out that they do not work. The computer can also show what will happen under different conditions – say to a bridge in various winds. Computers can also work out the most economical way of making something out of the materials available.

Computer monitors the temperature and controls pouring of molten metal in automated steel works.

Computer aided manufacture (CAM)

Machines that have to do the same thing over and over again can be operated automatically by a computer. The computer's program tells it how to control the machine and as software is easy to change this kind of control is very flexible. For example a lathe, used for turning and shaping things, can be programmed to move in various ways to make different products.

Computer control is also being applied to industrial processing, such as brewing, chemical manufacture, baking, oil refining and so on. Computers are very good at monitoring situations and responding to feedback. Heavy industries, such as mining and steel making, are using computers too.

Robots

Robots are automatic machines which can be programmed to carry out lots of different jobs. Most of the robots used in factories are

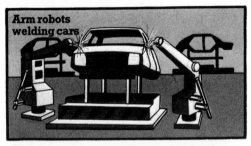

Arm robots welding cars

simply mechanical arms with a tool at the end, put to work on production lines. They cut, weld, rivet, paint, lift, pack and carry out many of the jobs necessary to make cars, washing machines, TVs and almost anything else. Robots are not intelligent, but simply move in response to instructions which take the form of a computer program. The computer runs the program and sends signals to the robot, making it move in the correct way to do what it is supposed to. Robots are very versatile and can perform

lots of different jobs if given new software and tools. For example a paint spraying robot can be "re-trained" to weld.

The latest robots are equipped with electronic sensors, such as video camera "eyes", microphone "ears", sonar or radar measuring and navigation devices and touch sensors. The robot uses these to send information back to its controlling computer. The computer is programmed to use this feedback to modify its instructions to the robot, in response to what is

Robots packing boxes

happening. A robot can be made to remove broken biscuits from a conveyor belt if it has a camera eye and its computer is programmed to recognize mishapen biscuits for instance.

Computer works out cutting program.

Rough design

Computer-controlled cutting robot.

Automatic sewing machine

Future applications

Eventually the most advanced systems will link together CAD, CAM, robots and other automated machinery. A computer will be used to get the best possible design for a product and then put this information into the program which instructs the computer-controlled machines and robots that are making the finished product. The example above shows how a designer might design a pair of shoes, use the computer to work out the best cutting pattern for different sizes and then program the cutting and sewing robots with this information.

The people in charge of a factory would not actually have to be there. They could instruct and monitor the machines from home or an office, using computers linked by telecommunications to the factory. Sensors on the robots and video cameras in the factory could be used to send information back to the staff to show what was happening.

Video technology

Video is a way of electronically recording pictures and sounds on tape or disc. Television studios use video for recording programmes and an increasing number of feature films are being put on video so that you can buy or rent them to watch at home on your TV set. Video tape is good for making home movies, too, as it is cheaper and easier to use than ordinary film. Discs are the latest video development and you can see here how they differ from tape.

Cameras and recorders

Pictured on the right is a portable, home video camera. When used with a video cassette recorder it will make tapes of what you shoot, or you can plug it directly into your TV for instant display.

The light and sound from the scene you are shooting is turned into a stream of electronic signals by the camera. The recorder changes these signals into magnetic pulses and records them on a magnetic tape cassette in the machine.

This camera has a tiny TV screen as its viewfinder.

Video cassette player/recorder

Sound is recorded on the edge of the tape and pictures diagonally in the middle.

Video cassette player/recorders

A video cassette player turns the magnetic pulses recorded on the tape back into electronic signals. These are turned into pictures and sound again by your TV set, just as broadcast TV signals are. Most home video cassette machines record as well as play tapes. You can use them to tape ordinary TV programmes to watch later. This is known as off-air taping. The machine does not get the broadcast signals from your TV set, but has its own built-in TV tuner and receiver. So you can watch a programme on one channel, while your recorder tapes another at the same time.

Moving pictures

Moving pictures are recorded on video as still pictures, called frames, one at a time. They are played back very fast (25 frames a second in the UK and Europe, 30 frames a second in the USA and Japan) to give the effect of a moving image. The player can freeze a single frame to show a still picture. You can also play the video at different speeds for slow and fast motion and run it backwards.

Video discs

Video discs are similar in shape and size to audio LPs. At the moment you can only play pre-recorded video discs, not record them yourself, and you need a special video disc player to do so (just like with audio tapes and discs).

There are two different types of video disc. One is recorded and played using a stylus in a similar way to audio discs. The other uses a thin laser beam. Laser discs look like silvery mirrors and reflect light in rainbow colours. As they are played by a laser beam which does not actually touch the disc, they cannot be worn out. The reflective layer which holds the recording is covered by a thin coating of clear plastic which lets the laser beam through, but makes the disc so tough it will play perfectly even when covered in scratches and fingerprints. The other sort of disc is black and rainbow-shiny but must not be handled and is kept in a protective sleeve.

Interactive video discs

When you play a video tape, you have to watch it in sequence, waiting while the tape runs fast if you want to miss a bit. With a disc, you have "random access" to any part of it, which means you can tell the player which frame you want and it will play it instantly. You can control the order of the frames and the way in which they are played, and this is called "interactive" or "active play" video.

Every frame is numbered, like the pages of a book, and they can be grouped together into chapters. You can call up individual frames or chapters, or tell the player in what sequence to play them. Still frames made up of text and illustrations can be recorded on the disc with the ordinary video sections. The still frames can include things like multiple choice questions on the previous chapter. If you give the wrong answer, the player may automatically offer to show the relevant part of the video again. Some players contain microchips for control and to monitor your responses. Interactive video discs are useful for education and training, and even used in shops as an animated catalogue of goods.

Playing laser discs

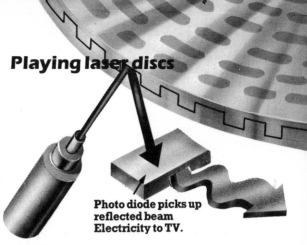

Photo diode picks up reflected beam Electricity to TV.

The picture and sound information is stored on the disc as a spiral of microscopic pits in a reflective layer, under the clear plastic coating. The laser beam in the player focuses on the reflective layer and is bounced back to a photo diode. The tiny pits change the reflection sent back to the photo diode, making it produce a varying current of electricity. This is turned by your TV back into the sound and pictures that were originally recorded. The information on laser discs is analogue, not digital as you might expect.

Computer control

Disc is played following instructions sent out by computer.

Disk drive plays computer program

Some video disc players can be controlled with a home computer. A program tells it which frames to show, when and how to play them, whether to change the speed, freeze or repeat a frame to alter the original video. With this sort of control, the information on a single video disc can be used in lots of different ways, simply by writing new software.

41

Microchips

Without microelectronics, and particularly the silicon chip, the information revolution would not be happening. Almost everything covered in this book works by microelectronics. Chips are so small and cheap to produce that they are making complex, versatile machines available to everyone.

Electronics

All electronic equipment – TVs, radios, phones, computers and so on – work because of tiny electric currents flowing round specially designed circuits. These circuits are formed from different kinds of components, such as transistors, diodes, capacitors and relays which control the flow of electricity through the circuit. The picture below compares the components you would need to make a simple radio circuit yourself, with a chip that does the same job.

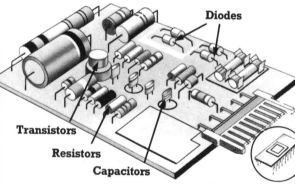

Diodes

Transistors

Resistors

Capacitors

Microelectronics and chips

Microelectronics is electronics on a microscopic scale. Thousands of minute components and circuits can be crammed onto a tiny microchip, also known as an integrated circuit, only a few millimetres square. Their smallness gives microchips several advantages. Obviously they take up less space and so lots of them can be fitted inside a machine, giving increased processing power. They also work faster because the electricity has only a tiny journey to make flowing round a microscopically small circuit. Another great advantage is that chips are cheap to make as they are produced in vast quantities.

What are chips?

This picture shows a close up of a "computer on a chip" of the kind used to make electronic machines "intelligent". All chips are made from wafer thin slices of chemicals called semi-conductors, the most commonly used is silicon. Semi-conductors conduct electricity – not as well as true conductors such as metals, but much better than non-conductors (called insulators) like wood.

Processing circuit where all the calculating is carried out. This is called the ALU (arithmetic and logic unit).

A microchip's circuits are etched into its surface. The components and pathways for electricity to flow along are formed by adding tiny amounts of conductors and insulators which change the conducting ability of the semi-conducting surface.

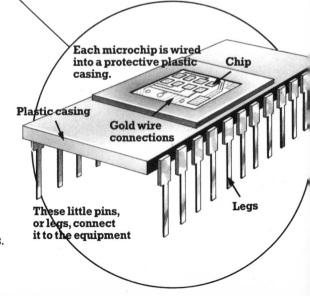

Each microchip is wired into a protective plastic casing.

Chip

Plastic casing

Gold wire connections

These little pins, or legs, connect it to the equipment

Legs

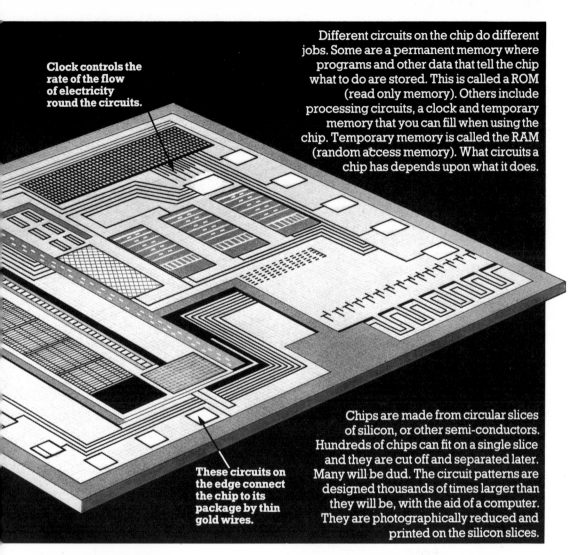

Clock controls the rate of the flow of electricity round the circuits.

Different circuits on the chip do different jobs. Some are a permanent memory where programs and other data that tell the chip what to do are stored. This is called a ROM (read only memory). Others include processing circuits, a clock and temporary memory that you can fill when using the chip. Temporary memory is called the RAM (random access memory). What circuits a chip has depends upon what it does.

These circuits on the edge connect the chip to its package by thin gold wires.

Chips are made from circular slices of silicon, or other semi-conductors. Hundreds of chips can fit on a single slice and they are cut off and separated later. Many will be dud. The circuit patterns are designed thousands of times larger than they will be, with the aid of a computer. They are photographically reduced and printed on the silicon slices.

Kinds of chips

There are many different kinds of chip, designed to do different jobs. A phone, for example, might have a modem chip to turn the incoming analogue signals into digital data, a memory chip to store phone numbers, control chips to carry out functions like automatic dialling and call routing, a character generating chip to work the VDU screen, a speech synthesizer chip and recording chips for messages, a laser chip in a fibre optic system and a microprocessor to organize and control them all.

Chips are programmed and given any special data they need to carry out their tasks when they are made. As they are specialized, or dedicated, in this way you could not take the chips out of a washing machine and use them in your home computer. However, the same design of chip can be programmed in many ways for different, but similar, uses.

Communicating with computers

In order to use the computerized new technology you have to be able to put in commands and information (known as input), get a response (known as output) and possibly store data for later use. There are lots of ways of communicating with computers and some are more obvious than others. A keyboard, for example, is more apparent than a pressure sensor that alerts a microprocessor if you do not put on your seat belt in a car. These pages look at some of the input, output and storage devices used with computers today.

Keyboards

Home computer

Alphanumeric keyboard

Typing at a keyboard is the most familiar way of inputting information. Home computers, terminals in banks and shops, videotex, phones and even digital watches all have some kind of keyboard. When you press a key this produces a coded electrical current that the computer recognizes as "b" or "B", "2" or a command such as "set the alarm". The kind of keyboard will depend upon the function of the machine. Many have letters and number plus special command keys.

Magnetic storage

Tapes, disks and stripes like those on bank cards are all ways of storing information magnetically. The digital data is sent to a recorder as pulses of electricity and these magnetize tiny particles of iron oxide on the surface of the tape, disk or stripe. "On" pulses make the particles face one way, "off" pulses make them face the other. The data is read by a magnetic sensor which turns the two magnetic fields back into electrical pulses. This is the most widespread way of storing computer data and it is erasable.

Disk

Tape in cassette

Reading

Computers can be taught to read but they have to memorize the shapes of all the characters (letters, numbers, symbols) for every different typeface they will come across. Computers read printing by scanning the page with a sensor. This produces on signals where ink is present and off signals where the page is blank and so the computer "sees" the characters as if they are 1s in a grid of 0s, like the picture above. Optical sensors work by reflecting light from the page and magnetic sensors read magnetic ink.

Pressure sensors

These can be used to "read" handwriting. The computer memorizes your signature if you sign your name several times, resting on a pressure sensitive pad. It turns the pressure and position of the pen into a digital number and can then compare these with your signature later, say on a cheque signed on another pressure sensor. Pressure sensors can also be used to tell if someone is sitting in a seat and to make a voice synthesizer chip speak to them, or to tell where someone is pointing on a touch sensitive screen.

Pressure sensitive pad tells the computer where the writing is.

FIRE!

Speech synthesis

Speech synthesizer chips have all the sounds that go to make up words stored in their memories. These sounds are known as phonemes. The chip produces them when letters are typed at a keyboard. Other chips have whole sentences digitally recorded in their memories and speak in response to certain input – the chip above is linked to a smoke detector, for example. Computerized telephones and exchanges use speech synthesis to pass on information to callers.

Hearing

Teaching a computer to understand speech is harder than getting it to talk. Although computers can be given electronic ears with simple microphones, it is difficult to program them to recognize complex sounds like speech, because people's voices are so variable. A computer can learn to recognize a few simple commands but it has to memorize every person's voice separately. An experimental dictation typewriter took 100 minutes to process and type a sentence that took just 30 seconds to say.

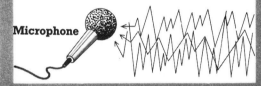

Microphone

Laser disc

Optical storage

These systems can use the same reflective material as audio and video laser discs. Digital data is stored as pits and flats (no pits) in the reflective layer. When scanned by a laser the pits and flats reflect the beam differently, producing on/off electrical signals in a photo diode. A single laser disc can hold half a million pages of writing. Bar codes are another kind of optical storage system where the on/off signals are produced by a light reflected on black and white stripes.

Computer control

Computer control is used with all sorts of machines and processes – robots, model railways, steel-making, washing machines, digital watches, calculators and telephone exchanges are just a few examples. The controlling computer may be a whole machine that can be reprogrammed to do any kind of job and control any other machine, or just a few, permanently built-in microprocessors and other chips pre-programmed and dedicated to doing a single thing.

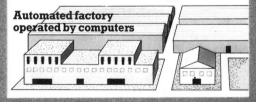

Automated factory operated by computers

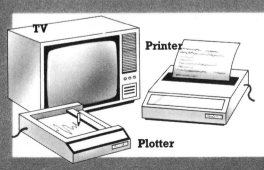

TV

Printer

Plotter

Writing and pictures

The most usual kind of output is writing and pictures – known as text and graphics. This can be displayed on a screen or printed or drawn by computer-controlled electronic machines like printers and plotters. Screens and printers are used with all kinds of computers, like those in shops.

Information revolution words

Access: Getting data out of a computer or its database.

Acoustic coupler: A kind of modem (see below) where the handset of the phone fits into two cups. The acoustic coupler turns computer data into sounds and vice versa.

Analogue: This word actually means "similar to", but in computing it means "smoothly changing" – the opposite of digital.

Automation: Making machines carry out jobs without the constant help of people. Automatic machines are often controlled by computer or microchips.

Bar code: A pattern of black and white stripes that represents digital data.

BASIC: A computer language used for writing computer programs. It stands for Beginner's All-purpose Symbolic Instruction Code.

Bit: A binary digit either a 0 or a 1. In a computer bits are represented by on/off pulses of electricity.

Byte: A group of eight bits. Bytes are used to represent single pieces of information, such as a number, letter or symbol.

Cellular telephones: A radio telephone system where small areas, called cells, are each covered by a radio transmitter and form a network of overlapping cells.

Chip: See microchip, below.

Computer: An electronic calculating machine that can process information and follows instructions given to it in the form of a program.

Data: This is another word for information, used particularly to refer to the information that a computer deals with.

Database: An electronic store of information that can be used in a variety of ways by computers.

DBS (direct broadcast by satellite): TV broadcast via satellite, picked up by your own dish aerial.

Disk: A magnetic, or "floppy", disk stores data for use with a computer. They are played and recorded on a machine called a disk drive.

Digital: This word means dealing with numbers. Computers can only work with digital information where everything has been turned into binary digits.

Diode: An electronic component that allows electricity to flow one-way only.

Direct coupler: A modem that connects a computer directly to the phone line, by-passing the handset.

Electronic funds transfer (EFT): Taking money from one bank account and putting it in another electronically, using computers and telecommunications.

Frame: A videotex page (see below) or any single screen-sized picture, such as the frames of a film or video.

Gateway: The link of a computer database into the viewdata system, so that people can look at the information in it.

Input: Information that is put into a computer for processing.

Integrated circuit (IC): Another name for a microchip.

Keyword search: A way of getting information from a database by giving the computer a key word or phrase to look up.

Laser: Laser light is made up of just one wavelength in a concentrated, straight beam. The word stands for, Light Amplification by Stimulated Emission of Radiation.

LCD (liquid crystal display): A kind of screen used to display information.

LED (light emitting diode): A diode (see above) which produces light in response to electricity.

Machine code: A computer language made up of the bits and bytes that a computer can actually understand.

Microchip: A tiny, electronic device containing many components and circuits etched onto the surface of a semi-conducting material like silicon.

Microwave: A kind of short radio wave used for telecommunications.

Modem: A device that turns computer data into a signal which can travel over the phone, and vice versa. The word is short for modulator/demodulator.

On-line: When a terminal, phone or other equipment is connected directly to a computer, it is said to be on-line.

Optical fibre: A very thin strand of glass or plastic that can carry light. Used in telecommunications.

Output: Information that comes out of a computer.

Packet switching: Sending messages as small, digital packets that can travel through a telecommunications system independently of each other. They are reassembled at the receiving end.

Page: A videotex term used to describe a screen-sized display of information. Also known as a frame.

Pixel: Short for picture cell. Screens are divided up into a grid of pixels and images are made by picture generating chips which light up the pixels in response to signals from a computer.

Program: A sequence of instructions which will make a computer carry out a job. They are written in computer languages such as BASIC and machine code.

Random access: When using a tape to store information you have to run it backwards and forwards to get to the parts you want. A random access system allows you to jump instantly from one part to another without waiting. Random access can be provided by memory circuits on a chip, by magnetic disks and laser discs.

Software: Another name for computer programs. The actual computer, which runs the software, is referred to as hardware.

Speech synthesis: Electronically generated speech which is made up from sounds that have been digitally recorded, often on chips.

Terminal: A computer keyboard, or other input device, that does not have its own computing power but is linked to a distant computer and database.

Telesoftware; Computer programs which are loaded straight into your computer by videotex. In Britain telesoftware is provided as viewdata on *Prestel* by *Micronet*, and as teletext by the BBC's *Ceefax. Comp-U-Serve* supplies viewdata telesoftware in North America.

Teletext: Broadcast information from distant computers which can be displayed on your TV screen. The two teletext services in Britain are *Ceefax*, run by the BBC, and *Oracle*, run by the ITV. In North America various teletext services are being offered on a trial basis, such as *keyfax, IRIS* and *Extravision*.

Videotex: Information from distant computers displayed on a TV screen. It can reach you as TV broadcasts (known as teletext) and by phone or cable TV (known as viewdata). As these are very new developments these terms may be used differently by other books and magazines. Videotex is often used to mean viewdata, for example.

Viewdata: A two-way communications system where you can get information from distant computers and respond to it. Viewdata works by phone, or by interactive cable TV. In Britain viewdata is called *Prestel*, in Canada it is called *Telidon*. North America has *Comp-U-Serve* and *The Source* which provide home computer owners with access to databases and services such as teleshopping and banking and electronic mail.

Voice message: A digitally recorded message that accompanies text and graphics on screen, or is played to pass on information automatically.

Word processor: A computer used for writing, editing, storing and manipulating typed text.

Work station: An electronic "desk" made up of a computer, phone and links to a central computer, database, other work stations and equipment like printers.

Index

Books to read

If you want to find out more about some of
the things mentioned in this book, such as
TV and video, computers and
programming, BASIC, chips and
electronics, here are some useful books to
read. They are all published by Usborne
Publishing.

TV & Video C. Griffin-Beale

Computers B. Reffin Smith

Understanding the Micro
    J. Tatchell & B. Bennett

Introduction to Computer Programming
    B. Reffin Smith

Computer Jargon L. Watts & C. Stockley

Better BASIC B. Reffin Smith & L. Watts

Inside the Chip H. Davies & M. Wharton

Fun With Electronics J. G. McPherson

ROBOTICS

Tony Potter and Ivor Guild

Designed by **Roger Priddy**

Consultant Editor: **Nigel East**
Editor: **Lynn Myring**
Robot program: **Chris Oxlade**

Illustrated by: Jeremy Gower
Chris Lyon, Simon Roulstone, Martin Newton,
Geoff Dicks, Mick Gillah, Rob McCaig,
Tim Cowdell, Janos Marffy, Mike Saunders,
Kuo Kang Chen, Stan North.

CONTENTS

About robotics

Seventy years ago no one had ever heard the word "robot". It was first used by a Czechoslovakian writer, Karel Capek (pronounced Chapek) in the 1920s. He wrote a play about a scientist who invents machines which he calls robots, from the Czech word *robota*, meaning "slave-like work". He gave them this name because they were used to do very boring work. At the end of the play, the robots kill their human owners and take over the world.

There are many robots in existence now, but they are quite different from the robots of science fiction films and books. Instead of being frightening, super-intelligent metal

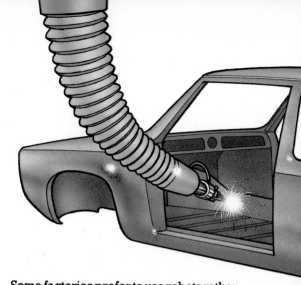

Some factories prefer to use robots rather than other automatic machines because they can be re-programmed to do different jobs.

people, real robots are just machines controlled by a computer to work in a set way. They are generally deaf, dumb, blind, have no sense of taste, smell or touch, have difficulty getting around, and have no intelligence of their own. However, advances in microchip technology mean that robots are beginning to be made with sensors – a TV camera "eye" or a microphone "ear" for instance – which give them very limited senses like electronic sight and hearing.

Robots are used to do many things, often jobs which are very dangerous or tiring for people to do, like welding car bodies. In factories, robots are useful because they are often able to work more efficiently than people. Although robots break down, they never need holidays, sleep or meal breaks.

Some robots are used to do jobs that would be impossible for people to do, such as working inside the radioactive part of a nuclear power station, or visiting distant planets. Others, like the small micro-robots used with a home computer, are just for fun or for learning about robotics. You can find out how to make your own micro-robot on page 86.

What robots can and cannot do

Robots are able to do many different things, especially in factories. Here robots are carefully maintained and organized to work alongside other automatic machines. Robots are rarely used to work outside because it is much more difficult to get them to work away from the ordered environment of a factory.

Science fiction robots are often made to look human, but the appearance and ability of an industrial robot depend on the kind of work it has to do. The majority of them are like "arms" bolted to the floor because the work they do can be done standing in one place. These arm robots are often called manipulative robots because they hold things – perhaps a tool like the welding torch in the picture below.

Arm robots are most familiar in car factories, but they can be found in many other industries – electronics, engineering, clothing and confectionery, for example. The jobs they are best at are those that involve doing the same thing over and over again.

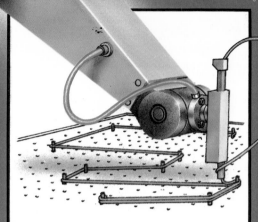

Accurate robots

Some robots are able to do very accurate and intricate work, but this depends on the design of the robot and the computer program that controls it. This picture shows a robot laying out lengths of wire in a complex pattern for wiring-up electric vehicles, like fork-lift trucks. To do this, it first has to push nails into holes in a pegboard according to a pattern stored in its computer memory. The robot has to line up the nails with the holes very precisely to get them to fit.

Robots today

Most of today's robots are only able to work in a factory where everything is carefully organized around them. Robots are usually next to a conveyor belt which "feeds" them with work, for example. They also have to be kept in a wire "cage" to prevent the robot from injuring any passing people. Some scientists believe that in fifty years or so it will be possible to build a robot capable of working anywhere. This kind of robot would have to be much more "intelligent" than existing robots and have lots of sensors to be able to react to a vast amount of information, or feedback, about the world around it. Even the best of today's robots could not react fast enough to catch a ball, for instance. Imagine trying to do this with thick mittens on, one hand tied behind your back, your eyes blindfolded, feet cemented to the ground and your ears and nose blocked up. Most robots have to rely on even less feedback than this.

Tough robots

Many robots can do work which would be dangerous or unpleasant for people. Robots are very tough because they are made of metal, and can withstand very extreme conditions, such as a hot poisonous atmosphere. This robot is putting its hand right into a red-hot oven to take a metal casting out. The heat does not affect its performance, so it is able to produce high quality castings by always taking them out at the right temperature.

What happens when things go wrong?

Many robots are unable to react to anything unexpected happening to them because they have no sensors. This robot, pictured below, is controlled by a computer to spray bicycle frames as they pass by on a conveyor. If a frame falls off, the robot carries on spraying. One way of preventing this is to put a switch on the conveyor which turns off the robot. Another way to stop it is to give the robot electronic senses to detect what is going on.

This robot wears a plastic cover as an "overall" to stop paint clogging it up. Other robots also need to wear special covers.

How strong is a robot?

The strength of a robot depends on the power of its motors and the materials it is made from. A home micro-robot made from thin sheet metal can only lift the weight of an apple, for example. But a large industrial robot like the one above could pick up something as heavy as an elephant. A robot like this can easily lift sacks all day, whereas even a strong person would get tired eventually.

Mobile robots

A mobile robot is a computer-controlled vehicle of some kind, and the most common have wheels or tracks. Some carry a computer around with them, but others are connected to a computer by a long cable or by radio link. Mobile robots are beginning to be used in factories to move goods and materials around, sometimes from one arm robot to another. Robot trucks like the one in the picture below can be guided round the factory by following white lines or magnetic signals from cables buried underground. The computer controlling the truck is programmed to tell it which route to take round the network of lines or cables.

Steering a robot

This is a micro-robot called Bigtrak. It is steered by two motors driving the wheels in the centre. Its computer controls the steering by changing the speed and direction of the motors. Bigtrak's other wheels just prevent it tipping up.

How robots follow buried cables

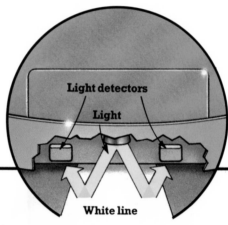

Light detectors

Light

White line

How robots follow lines

The circle above shows how a robot can follow lines by using a sensor to send feedback to the computer about its position over the line. The sensor usually consists of a light pointing to the floor with a light detector either side of it. These detect light reflected from the line. If the robot steers off the line, they send a message to the computer to correct the steering.

Bumper   Sensor

Cable

Magnetic field

A cable-following robot like the one above usually has two coils of wire fixed to the front which detect a magnetic field surrounding the buried cable. The magnetic field is made by sending electricity through the cable and this field, in turn,

creates a small electric current in the robot's coils. The strength of the current in the coils alters according to how far the robot is from the cable. The computer steers the robot over the cable by balancing the strength of current in the two coils.

  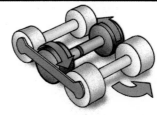

Forwards or backwards: Both wheels are driven at the same speed in the same direction.

Right turn: The left-hand wheel is driven forwards, and the right-hand wheel backwards.

Left turn: The right-hand wheel is driven forwards, and the left-hand wheel backwards.

Robots with tracks can be steered like this too because each track is like a driven wheel.

Steering mechanism

This kind of robot steers by turning on the spot. Robots can also be steered gradually as they move forward by making both motors go forward, with one going faster.

Some robots use a steering mechanism like that in a car. Instead of a steering wheel they have a motor connected to a computer. Robots like this are less manoeuvreable than the Bigtrak type because they cannot turn on the spot.

Roving robot

New mobile robots are being developed which find their way around by navigation. This means that the robot's computer has to decide how to get the robot from where it is to where it wants to go without following any guides, like white lines, and without bumping into anything.

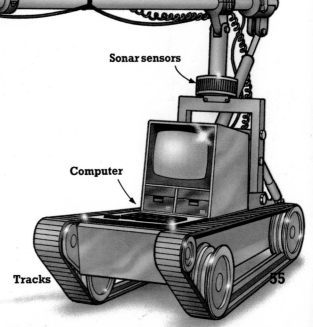

Grab arm

Sonar sensors

Computer

Tracks

This picture shows an experimental robot called Mr Bill (Mr stands for Mobile Robot) which navigates by using sensors to find out about its environment. Most of the information comes from sonar sensors mounted on the robot. These work by emitting a sound, and then "listening" for an echo to bounce back from obstacles. This information is compared with a "map" of the positions of fixed obstacles, like walls, which is stored in the memory of the on-board computer. There are also other sensors on the robot's wheels, called odometers, which tell the computer how far the robot has travelled. The computer works out where the robot is by making calculations using all this information.

55

How arm robots work

These pages show all the things that are needed to make an arm robot work and a view inside the robot to show what makes it move. There are many different ways of constructing and powering a robot. This one is jointed like a human arm and is driven by electric motors. Some industrial robots work in the same way, but are much more complex inside.

Each moving part of a robot is usually driven by a separate source of power. This one has six motors to make its arm and wrist parts move. Each motor is switched on and off by the computer, which also controls the speed of the motors. You can find out about other ways of driving robots on page 72.

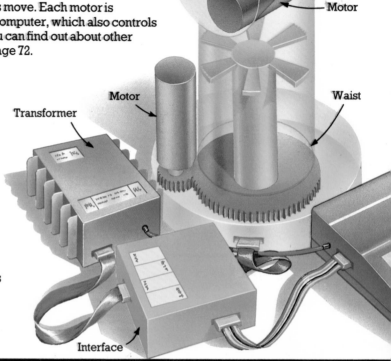

Shoulder

Gear

Motor

Motor

Waist

Transformer

Electricity for the robot's motors and computer is provided by a transformer. This converts the strong electric voltage from the mains into a low voltage

Transformer

Interface

A device called the interface links the transformer, motors and computer together. Inside is an electronic circuit which switches the power to the motors on and off when instructed by the computer.

Interface

Arm movements

Waist

Shoulder

Elbow

Most arm robots have three main parts which are joined together. The point where one part is fixed to another is usually called a joint or axis. The joints on a robot like the one above are given the names elbow, shoulder and waist. Each axis is said to give the robot one degree of freedom because it allows the parts fixed at the joint to move in a certain way. In these pictures you can see the direction in which each joint allows the robot to move.

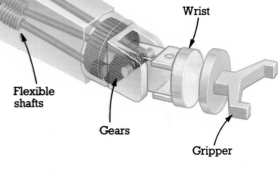

There are three tiny motors inside the robot's "forearm" which drive three moving parts in the wrist. These motors are connected to gears in the wrist by very long shafts. Each shaft has a flexible joint in the middle which allows it to bend as the wrist moves from side to side and up and down.

Elbow

Motors

Wrist

Each motor is connected by gears to a shaft which moves part of the robot. In this picture the shafts are the parts painted orange, and the gears are painted green. The gears help to reduce the speed of the motors.

Flexible shafts

Gears

Gripper

The computer is programmed using the keyboard. It controls everything the robot does by sending a sequence of instructions to the interface.

The robot's hand, called a gripper, is shown separated from its wrist in this picture. You can find out how these work on page 74. The wrist is a complicated mechanism which can bend in three ways, shown in the picture below. Some robots have wrists which bend in only two directions, but this depends on the kind of work they have to do. The more joints in the wrist, the more able the robot is to make fine movements to do a job.

Wrist movements

Roll

Pitch

Yaw

Between the gripper and the end of the robot arm is a kind of wrist. Like the arm, the wrist usually has three joints, or axes of rotation. These allow the gripper to move in three ways, shown in the pictures above. These movements have special names: yaw, pitch and roll. A robot like this which can make six kinds of movements has six degrees of freedom. Some robots have more than this, some less, depending on the kind of work they do.

Designing robots

It is very difficult to design and build a robot, even to do a simple job. A robot designer has to begin by breaking down the job into as many steps as possible to see what sort of robot is needed. For example, the robot arm below would need to be able to bend its wrist if it had to lift a glass of water. These pages shown an imaginary robot servant designed to do all the dusting in a two-storey house. An extremely complex robot is needed to do this apparently simple task. Experts think it may be possible to build a robot like this in a few years time.

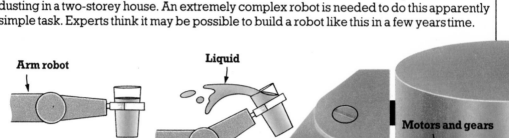

Arm robot

Liquid

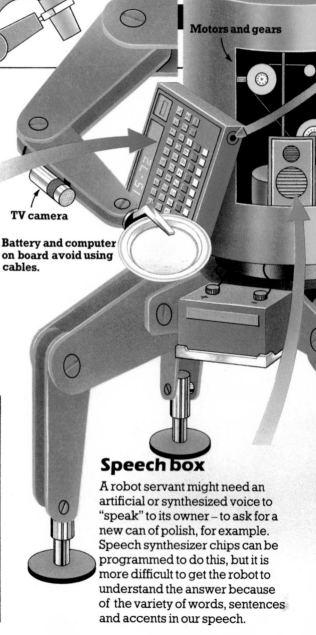

Motors and gears

Computer control

The computer has to be programmed to control everything the robot does: how the motors drive its legs and arms, how it navigates around the house without causing damage, the way it does its dusting, and so on. The computer must make the robot do everything in the right order, such as opening doors before going through them. It also has to work things out without delay so that the robot can respond instantly to something unexpected, like a baby crawling under its feet.

TV camera

Battery and computer on board avoid using cables.

The program

An extremely complex program would be needed for the computer because the robot's job involves hundreds of choices based on information, or data, about the world around it. This part of the design, called the software, gives the robot "intelligence" so that it can "decide" what to do.

Speech box

A robot servant might need an artificial or synthesized voice to "speak" to its owner – to ask for a new can of polish, for example. Speech synthesizer chips can be programmed to do this, but it is more difficult to get the robot to understand the answer because of the variety of words, sentences and accents in our speech.

Arms

The robot has two arms because it needs to be able to hold things while dusting underneath. It could also have a spray-can of polish, with a computer-controlled plunger to press the button, fixed to one arm. This would avoid the need for a third arm to hold the can.

Can of polish

Design your own robot

Try drawing a robot to do one of these jobs: **1** Take a dog for a walk. **2** Wash the dishes. **3** Mend a puncture in a bicycle tyre.

Sensors

Different kinds of sensors are required for the robot to do its job: navigation sensors to find its way around, TV camera "eyes" to so that it can "see" what is doing, and safety touch sensors which stop it if it accidently bumps into anything. All the data from the sensors is sent to the computer via an interface so that it can control the robot's actions.

Legs

This robot needs at least four legs to climb the steep stairs of a house – something it could not do with wheels or tracks. A Japanese designer has actually built a four-legged, stair climbing robot.

Walking robots

This shows what happens when a robot is built with different numbers of legs.

One leg

A one-legged robot like this has to keep hopping to balance, so it would not be much good for a job like dusting.

Two legs

When a two-legged robot takes one foot off the ground to walk, it has to balance on one foot. This is very difficult for the computer to control.

Three legs

A three-legged robot is very stable standing still, but as soon as it takes one foot off the ground to walk it falls over.

Four legs

A four-legged robot walks by moving one leg at a time. This means it always has three legs on the ground to balance with.

Special purpose robots

These pages show robots which have been specially designed by carefully working out all the things they need to be able to do for particular jobs. Sometimes factory arm robots can be adapted, but other jobs may need a completely new kind of design.

Sheep shearer

This is an experimental robot specially designed to shear sheep. The sheep is held down with straps on a cradle and shorn with electric clippers. The robot's computer gets feedback from sensors on the clippers so that it is able to position them just above the sheep's skin. If the sheep wriggles it can react in less than one ten-thousandth of a second to move the clippers away. An electronic "map" of the sheep's shape is stored in the computer's memory so that it can tell the robot where to cut.

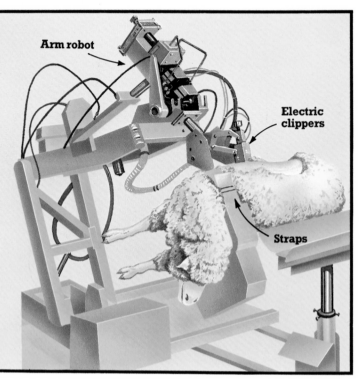

Arm robot

Electric clippers

Straps

Robot patient

This robot patient is designed to respond to treatment by students and can even "die" if someone makes a mistake. Computer-controlled electronic components inside the robot can be programmed to mimic breathing, heart-beat and blood pressure. Sensors inside the body measure the efficiency of a student's treatment.

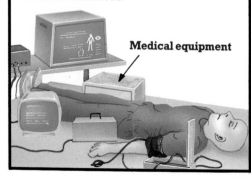

Medical equipment

Robot hand

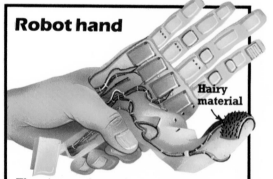

Hairy material

The picture above shows an experimental microchip-controlled false hand, which is activated by muscles in the wearer's arm. There is a microphone in the thumb covered by a strip of hairy material. The microphone "listens" for the rustling sound the material makes when an object is held. As the hairs are crushed, the sound stops, which tells the computer the grip is tight enough.

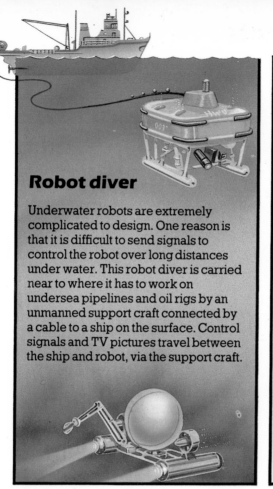

Robot diver

Underwater robots are extremely complicated to design. One reason is that it is difficult to send signals to control the robot over long distances under water. This robot diver is carried near to where it has to work on undersea pipelines and oil rigs by an unmanned support craft connected by a cable to a ship on the surface. Control signals and TV pictures travel between the ship and robot, via the support craft.

Walking robot

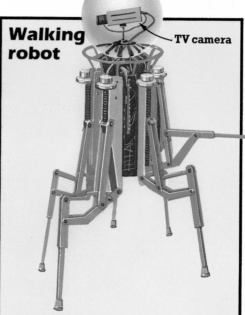

TV camera

This robot is able to walk over rough ground and go up stairs by adjusting the length of its legs. Inside the plastic dome at the top is a TV camera which sends pictures to a computer in the middle of the robot. The robot can walk around for about an hour before its batteries go flat.

Robotics teacher

Hero 1 is a robot designed to teach people at school or in industry about robotics. It is a mobile and arm robot combined and has lots of different sensors so that students can discover what they are and how they work. It also has a voice synthesizer which can be programmed with its built-in computer.

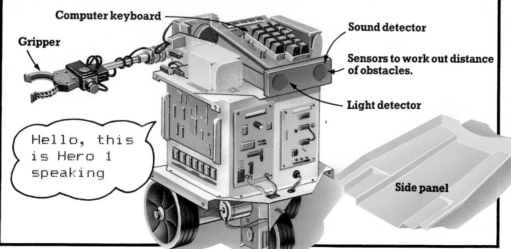

Computer keyboard

Gripper

Sound detector

Sensors to work out distance of obstacles.

Light detector

Hello, this is Hero 1 speaking

Side panel

Robots are particularly useful for doing jobs in space because it is such a hostile environment for humans to work in. In the future, robots and other automatic machines may make up most of the space workforce.

Space arm robot

The Space Shuttle can be fitted with a long, folding arm robot as part of its equipment. This is used for launching satellites and other machines from its cargo hold, or retrieving them from space for repair. The arm folds neatly out of the way in the cargo hold after use.

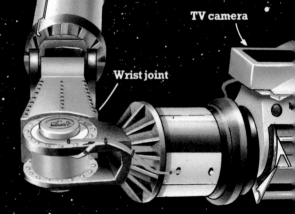

TV camera

Shoulder joint

Cargo hold

Elbow joint

Shiny blanket

The arm, called RMS (Remote Manipulator System), has its own computer which is programmed to make 20 different sets of movements. It can also be controlled from the flight deck with joysticks similar to those used with computer games. Up to eight cameras can be positioned on the arm so that the operator can see what to do.

The RMS is capable of lifting an object which would weigh about the same as fifteen cars on Earth. It is designed to cope with twice as much in an emergency. If the arm gets stuck and prevents the cargo doors from closing it can be jettisoned into space.

A shiny blanket covers the whole arm so that it reflects the Sun's heat and does not get too hot. There are also heating elements inside the blanket to keep the arm warm when the Shuttle is on the night side of Earth.

Each joint is driven by a tiny electric motor. Sensors on the joints tell the computer the position of the arm.

TV camera

Wrist joint

Satellites

Satellites often include components like sensors and computers, but are really automatic machines rather than robots. The sensors on satellites are often used to collect data rather than to provide feedback for its computer.

Stretched out, the arm can reach nearly as far as the length of two buses put together.

Robot missiles

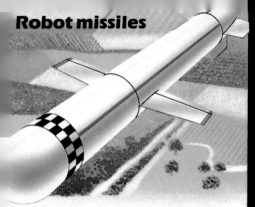

Some kinds of missiles are described by experts as robots. They are programmed to reach a target automatically using sensors and an on-board computer. Cruise missiles, for example, use sensors to "see" the ground below, and then compare this data with a computerized route map. This enables them to fly very low to avoid radar detection.

Space probes

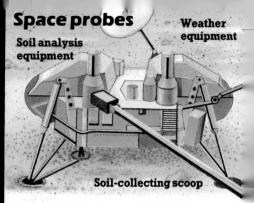

Soil analysis equipment

Weather equipment

Soil-collecting scoop

Apart from the moon, exploration of other planets in the solar system and beyond has only been made by robot spacecraft. This is mostly because of the time it takes to reach them – Voyager 1 took 18 months to reach Jupiter, for example. This picture shows a computer-controlled robot landing craft sent to the surface of Mars by Viking 1.

How the arm picks things up

The end of the arm has a special gripping mechanism inside, made of diagonally crossed wires, to hold satellites and other cargo. Each piece of cargo has a shaft sticking out of one end. The end of the arm is manoeuvred over the shaft, and then rotated. This twists the wires around the shaft so that the cargo is pulled tightly against the end of the arm. The end of the arm is simply rotated in the opposite direction to release the shaft.

The picture below shows the arm releasing a telecommunications satellite into orbit above the Earth.

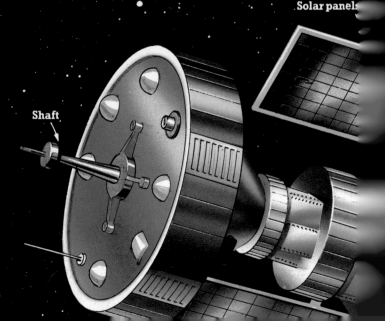

Solar panels

Shaft

End gripper

Micro-robots

A micro-robot is a small robot controlled by a home computer. You can find out how to make your own micro-robot on page 86.

Drawing robot

The Turtle is a mobile robot which can be programmed to draw with a pen as it moves around. A computer language called LOGO makes the robot move in units of about 1.5mm at a time. LOGO uses commands like "F 10" for forward 10 units, or "R 90" for right 90 degrees, to draw simple shapes like squares or triangles. The commands are used to combine a series of simple shapes to make pictures.

Each unit the Turtle moves is measured by a sensor mounted over a cog on each wheel. A tiny lamp on one side shines a beam of light between the teeth of the cog into a photoelectric cell on the other side. The teeth break the beam of light as the wheel rotates. Each break in the light path is detected by the photoelectric cell, which sends a message to the computer to count one unit.

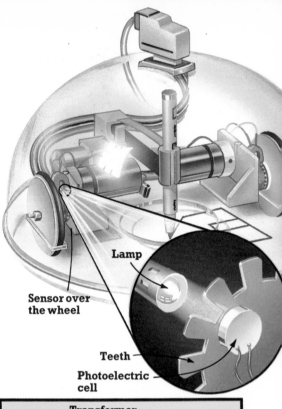

Lamp

Sensor over the wheel

Teeth

Photoelectric cell

How to connect up a micro-robot

These pictures show how a micro-robot arm is connected to a home computer and to a power supply.

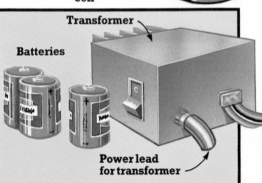

Transformer

Batteries

Power lead for transformer

Most micro-robots are driven by low voltage electric motors, so a transformer or batteries are used to power them. This power supply is usually connected to an electronic interface.

Port

It is very dangerous to plug a micro-robot into mains electricity.

Wires, known as control lines, which control the robot's motors, are plugged into a socket in the computer, called a port. (Not all home computers have the right ports to be able to do this.) One wire is often used for each motor.

Bar codes laid out in a long line.

Draw like the Turtle

Try drawing the shape these LOGO commands make. Use 1mm units for the forward movements. F100, R90, F100, R90, F100, R90, F100.

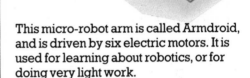

Gears to move arm

Motors

The interface is connected to the robot's motors. It is made of electronic components which switch the power to the motors on and off when the computer sends signals to them. Sometimes this circuit is in a separate box, but it can be inside the robot or the computer.

This micro-robot arm is called Armdroid, and is driven by six electric motors. It is used for learning about robotics, or for doing very light work.

Buggy

The robot on the left is called the BBC Buggy. It is made from Fischertechnic construction kit parts, so it can be added to by building extra bits, like an arm, on top.

A sensor, called an infra-red transceiver, is fixed to the front. This works by transmitting invisible infra-red light down to the ground, and then receiving it back when it is reflected by the surface the robot travels over.

The computer can be programmed to use the data from the infra-red transceiver to "see" a line, and tell the robot to follow it, or "read" a bar code like the one in the picture. The computer translates the bar code into musical notes and can play a tune by going over a series of codes laid on the floor. Different kinds of sensors can be plugged into the front of the circuit board on top of the Buggy. Bumpers make the robot reverse automatically when it bumps into something.

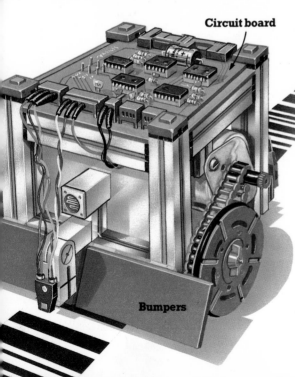

Circuit board

Bumpers

65

Robot factory workers

It is likely that very soon there will be almost totally unmanned factories. Perhaps just one or two people will program or monitor the computers and carry out routine maintenance to robots and other machines.

Car plants are currently among the most highly automated factories in the world. This picture shows how robots and other automatic machines, like conveyor belts and stackers, are used alongside each other to assemble and manufacture parts for cars.

Welding station

The framework built over the conveyor, shown on the right is called a welding station. It has six robots fixed to it holding welding guns. As car body panels, which have been lightly tacked together elsewhere in the factory, pass below, the robots weld them together to make a tough, rigid car bodies. As there are six robots working together, they can assemble cars very quickly.

Machining centre

The robots below are part of a system called a machining centre, or cell. One robot unloads heavy lumps of steel ready for the other robot which "serves" the two automatic lathes. A computer is in charge of the computers controlling the robots, lathes and conveyors to make sure each machine does the right thing at the right time. This is very important because otherwise the robots could collide, or damage the lathes.

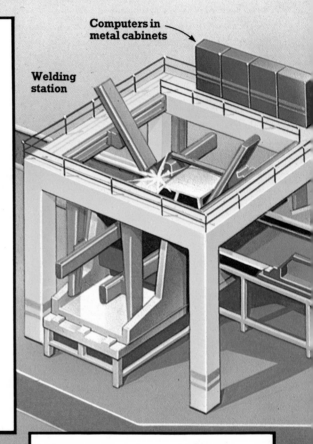

Computers in metal cabinets

Welding station

Lathe

Finished parts

Conveyor belts

Lathe

Pallet

Steel

The computer-controlled lathes could be programmed to make many different parts – for gearboxes, axles, engines and so on. The "serving" robot loads the raw steel into the lathes and then unloads the finished part onto the conveyor for assembly or finishing in another part of the factory.

The robot on the left unloads the steel from an automatic shuttle, which is like a tiny flat truck on rails. The truck carries the steel on a pallet – a wooden or metal platform used to stack materials for transport.

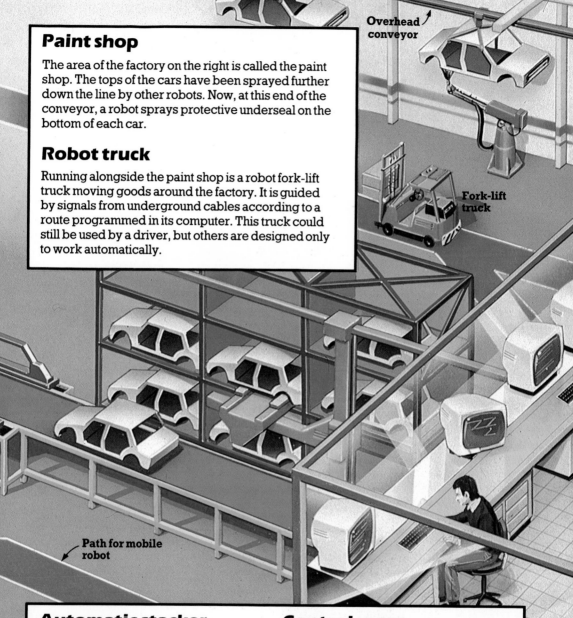

Paint shop

The area of the factory on the right is called the paint shop. The tops of the cars have been sprayed further down the line by other robots. Now, at this end of the conveyor, a robot sprays protective underseal on the bottom of each car.

Robot truck

Running alongside the paint shop is a robot fork-lift truck moving goods around the factory. It is guided by signals from underground cables according to a route programmed in its computer. This truck could still be used by a driver, but others are designed only to work automatically.

Overhead conveyor

Fork-lift truck

Path for mobile robot

Automatic stacker

The orange machine above is called an automatic stacker. It is programmed to place partly completed cars in a rack until they are needed. It saves floor space because it stacks things vertically. The same kind of computer-controlled stacker is used in Japanese cities to park bicycles. Some experts say these are robots because they can be programmed to stack different things, but others disagree.

Control room

Above is the control room where all the automatic operations being carried out in the factory are controlled and monitored. The computers here organize all the separate computers controlling the robots and other machinery. Someone watches display screens to check that all the machines are working properly and that production targets are met. Systems like this are already in use.

How to teach a robot

A robot's computer has to be given a set of instructions called a program to get it to work. This is done either by guiding the robot through a sequence of movements, and programming the computer to remember them, or by instructing the computer directly with the keyboard. In this way, the robot can be made to "learn" a set of movements, and repeat them over and over again.

Sensors

Remote teaching

Robots can be taught remotely with a computer keyboard, or a simplified keyboard called a teach pendant. This is connected to the computer and has commands like UP, DOWN, LEFT and RIGHT, which can be used to manouevre the robot. It also has a TEACH button which is pressed to make the computer to remember positions the operator wants it to know.

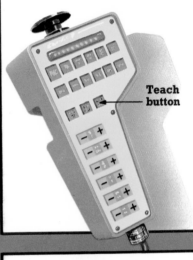

Teach button

Showing an arm robot what to do

One way of teaching a robot is by guiding its arm through the movements needed to do a job. This is called lead-through programming. The robot in this picture is being taught to spray paint by a person skilled at the job.

First the computer is programmed to remember the movements shown to the robot, and the order they were made in. Then the computer is programmed to make the robot automatically follow the path it was taught. It is very important that the computer repeats this exactly, otherwise the robot would spray paint in the wrong pattern and make a mess. Sensors on joints send data to computer about robot's position.

Direct control

Forward 10
Left 90
Forward 24
Left 45
Forward 35

This micro-robot is called the Zeaker. It can be programmed to move around, using a computer language with similar commands to LOGO. It can also be used for drawing as there is a pen fixed under its body.

Talking to robots

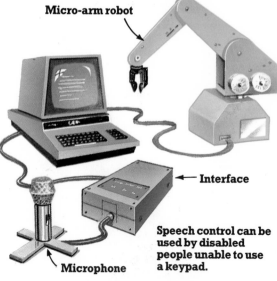

Micro-arm robot

Interface

Speech control can be used by disabled people unable to use a keypad.

Microphone

People are experimenting with controlling robots by giving them spoken instructions. This is done by connecting a microphone to the computer via a special interface. The interface converts commands such as "up" or "down" into a sequence of electrical signals which the computer is programmed to recognize as instructions for the robot.

The program, or software, which comes with the Zeaker lets the user direct its movements by pressing keys on the computer. A sequence of movements can be built up in the computer's memory and repeated over and over again to get the robot to draw complex patterns.

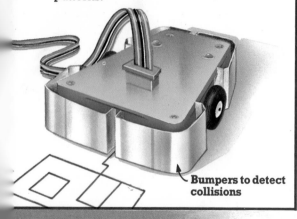

Bumpers to detect collisions

Chocolate-box packer

For some jobs, like picking things up and putting them down, the robot only needs to know precisely the points to start and finish at. The robot can be shown what to do by being guided to these points, by hand or with a teach pendant, and then getting its computer to remember them. The computer is programmed to work out the route the robot takes between the points. Industrial robots are taught to do loading and simple assembly jobs in this way.

In a factory the box would be on a conveyor.

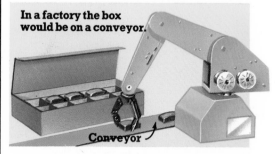

Conveyor

Step 1: The robot is guided to the chocolate and its computer told to remember the point where it has to open and close its gripper.

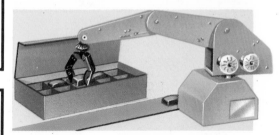

Step 2: The robot is guided to the point where it has to drop the chocolate into the box, and the computer instructed to remember it.

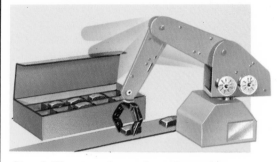

Step 3: The stopping and starting points are now in the computer's memory and it can tell the robot to repeat the movement over and over again.

Types of arm robot

There are five main types of arm robot, each designed to be able to move in different ways according to how its moving parts are put together. The design of a robot is called its architecture, and the space it can move around in as a result of its design is called its working envelope – shaded blue on these pages.

Jointed-arm robot

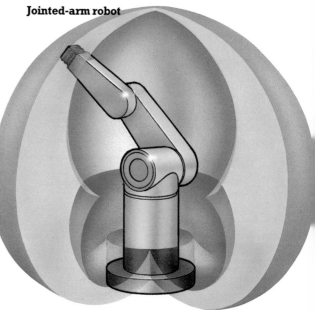

Jointed-arm robot

Jointed-arm robots

The design of a jointed-arm robot is based on the human arm. The one on the right has a rotating base part which is not able to go all the way round. The arm is jointed at the shoulder and elbow and can bend like a door hinge at both joints. The working envelope of a jointed-arm robot is shaped like part of a ball.

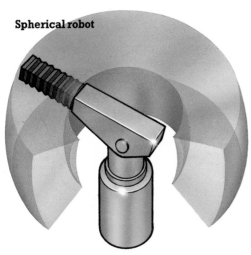

Spherical robot

Spherical or Polar robots

This type of robot gets its name from the spherical working envelope it is able to move in. The main arm part of the robot on the left moves in and out like a telescope, and also has a hinge-like joint at the shoulder. The robot's waist rotates, but it cannot go round 360°. The design of spherical robots makes them very strong, so they are often used to pick up heavy weights – sometimes as much as the weight of a car.

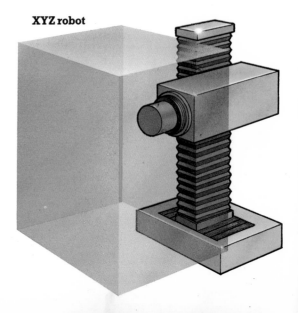

XYZ robot

XYZ robots

Robots like the one on the right get their name because they are able to move in three different directions called X, Y and Z and have a cube-shaped working envelope. The robot's side to side movement on its base is called direction X. The main arm part goes in and out telescopically, and this is direction Y. This part of the arm also moves up and down in direction Z. The design of XYZ robots makes them very accurate, so they are often used to do precise jobs like assembling things.

Cylindrical robots

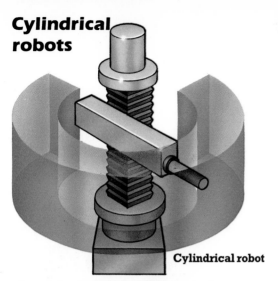

Cylindrical robot

The main arm part of a cylindrical robot moves in and out telescopically, and is also fixed to a "pole" at the shoulder so that it can slide up and down. The "pole" rotates, although not all the way round, and this gives the robot a working envelope shaped like a cylinder.

Spine robot

This is a new type of robot designed on the same principle as the human spine. The Spine robot can reach almost anywhere within its working envelope, even back into the centre, so it can work in inaccessible spaces like the inside of a car. The arm can also swing right round in a circle over and over again.

Your working envelope

Try working out the volume of your own working envelope by imagining that you are standing inside a cylinder with one arm stretched out to the side and the other straight above you. Get a friend to make the measurements shown in the picture and put them in place of the letters in the formula. Your answer should be in cubic centimetres or cubic inches, depending on which kind of measurements you use.
Formula: $3.14 \times A \times A \times B = ?$

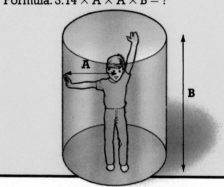

Inside its concertina cover are lots of discs piled on top of each other. The robot can be made longer or shorter by adding or removing discs. The discs are held together by two pairs of cables which are fixed to pistons in the base. The robot's computer controls the spine by moving the pistons to pull on the cables.

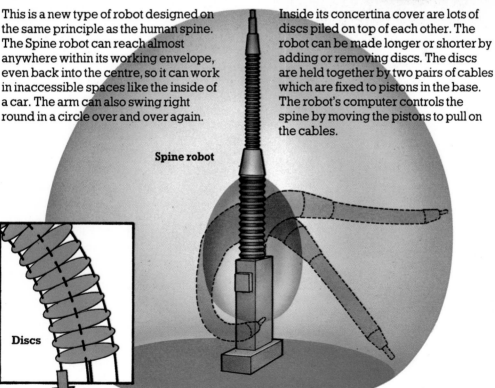

Spine robot

Discs

Cables

How robots are driven

Each moving part of a robot is driven separately, either by an electric motor or by a hydraulic or pneumatic system. The speed of the drive must be able to be varied so that the robot can be controlled to move quickly or slowly. Mobile robots are usually electrically driven, but the kind of drive used on an arm robot depends on the work it has to do.

Electric motors

Many different types of electric motor are used to drive robots. One type, which is often used, is called a direct current or d.c. motor. The picture below shows how a simplified d.c. motor looks inside. The gear at the bottom of the shaft that goes through the centre of the motor would be connected to part of a robot to drive it.

On either side of the motor are permanent magnets, one with a north and the other with a south pole facing the centre. Electricity is passed through the brown contact on the right, round the wire coil, out through the contact on the left and back to the battery. This makes the coil an electromagnet, with a north pole on one side (shown in green) and a south pole on the other (shown in yellow).

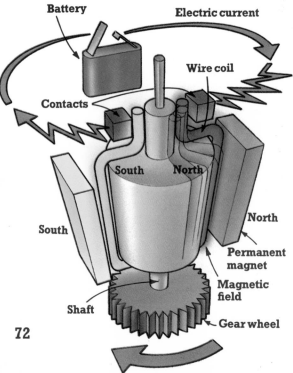

Battery

Electric current

Wire coil

Contacts

South North

South

North

Permanent magnet

Magnetic field

Shaft

Gear wheel

Hydraulic systems

A hydraulic system works rather like a syringe used for injections. It can be used to make either circular or straight movements according to the type.

End of robot arm

Hydraulic oil

The simplest kind is made up of a cylinder containing liquid, with a plunger, called a piston, at both ends. Because liquids cannot be compressed, when one piston is pushed in the other moves out. A system like this has to be fixed to each moving part of the robot – one like this would make the arm go in and out telescopically. Hydraulic systems are often used on robots designed to lift heavy weights.

Hydraulics are also often used instead of electric motors where there is a danger that sparks from a motor might ignite fumes in the atmosphere of a factory.

Because these poles are the same as the permanent magnets opposite them, the wire coil is repelled. When the coil is forced round half a turn, the parts touching the contacts will have changed positions, which again gives the coil a north pole on the right and a south pole on the left. The permanent magnets repel the coil again, and the whole process is repeated, over and over again.

The speed of a motor like this can be reduced or increased using gears. The speed can also be varied electrically with a device similar to the foot control on an electric sewing machine. The strength of a robot partly depends on the speed of its motors – usually the slower the motor the more power it has.

There are different ways of pushing the pistons in and out on a hydraulic system – the type used on car brakes, for example, is operated by a person pressing the brake pedal. On a robot, however, the piston has to be pushed by some electrically operated device for the computer to be able to control it. This picture shows a device called a solenoid fixed to a shaft on the end of the piston. This too has a piston inside which is pushed in and out by an electromagnet. You can see how these work on page 75

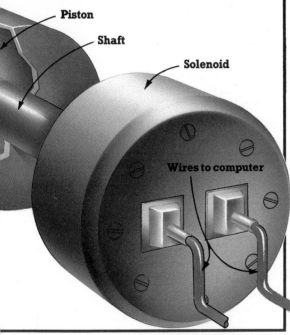

Piston

Shaft

Solenoid

Wires to computer

Pneumatic systems

In a pneumatic system, air, or some other gas, is used to move a mechanical part of the robot, often the gripper. A simple system consists of a cylinder with a piston inside which is connected to a shaft on the robot. Compressed air is let into one end of the cylinder by a computer-controlled electric valve. The air forces the piston forwards, which in turn moves the jaws of the gripper. Pneumatic systems are often used for grippers because gases compress and make the jaws "springy".

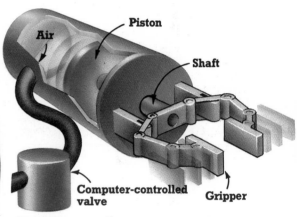

Air

Piston

Shaft

Computer-controlled valve

Gripper

How to make your own pneumatic gripper

You need: an empty detergent bottle, ice-cream or margarine tub, balloon, two pencils, thick card, tape, two fine nails or pins, sharp knife, scissors.

1. Carefully hammer nails through pencils half way along. Wiggle them around to make them loose. Cut two squares of card as shown.

2. Cut holes in front and lid of tub in the places shown here, with sharp knife.

3. Tape card to ends of pencils and push pencils through holes in the front of tub. Make sure nails are vertical and tape them to front of tub.

4. Remove cap of detergent bottle and put balloon on top. Push through hole in lid and between pencils. Squeeze bottle to inflate balloon and move "jaws".

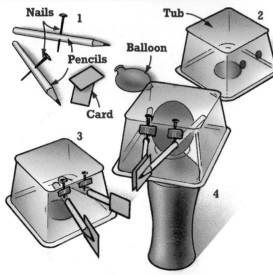

Nails   1

Pencils

Balloon

Tub   2

Card

3

4

73

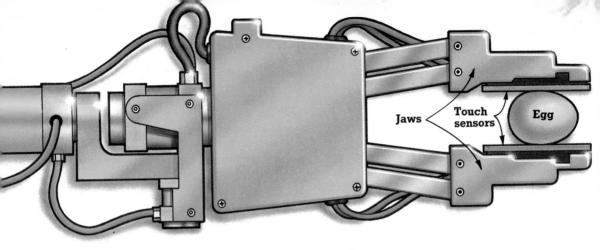

Jaws   Touch sensors   Egg

How robots hold things

Arm robots need a gripper, called an end effector, or another kind of tool fixed to their wrist to be able to do any work. There are many different kinds of grippers and tools and they are often specially designed to do a particular job. These pages explain what some of them are and how they work.

Hands

Some robots have grippers with jaws for grasping things. The picture above shows a gripper with two jaws holding an egg. These have to be able to hold an object without either crushing it or letting it slip. This is difficult to control, the pressure must be right otherwise the robot tends to fling the object out of its grasp when it moves quickly. The jaws in the picture have touch, or tactile, sensors on them which tell the computer how tightly they are gripping so that the correct pressure can be applied.

How robots change tools

A robot may need different tools to do a job and its computer can be programmed to make it change them automatically. The robot below holds tools with a bayonet fitting, like a light-bulb holder, attached to its wrist. The robot lowers the tool to be changed into a cradle, which holds it while the robot twists its wrist and pulls its arm away. The whole process is reversed to pick up another tool for the next stage in a job.

Bayonet fitting   Tools

Cradle

Tool

Holding hands

Try inventing different ways for a robot to hold things. One unusual method which has been used is to give the robot "sticky fingers" with glue pads.

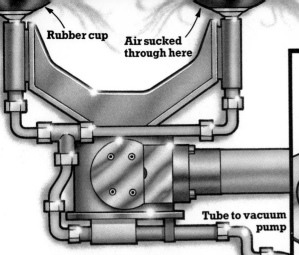

Rubber cup

Air sucked through here

Tube to vacuum pump

Vacuum grippers

Vacuum grippers, like the ones above, are often used to pick up fragile objects – glass, or paper sacks, for example. The grippers are rubber cups and air is sucked through them in much the same way as a vacuum cleaner. This makes the object stick to the gripper. The flow of air is controlled by the computer and the weight the grippers are able to lift depends on how powerful the suction is.

Holding tools

Many kinds of tools can be bolted directly to the robot's wrist. The robot below, for example, has a small electric grinder fixed to its wrist to take rough edges off pieces of metal. This method of holding a tool is used where the robot has to do the same job over and over again without the need for a tool change.

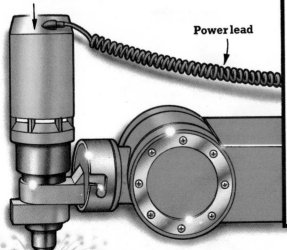

Electric grinder

Power lead

Magnet grippers

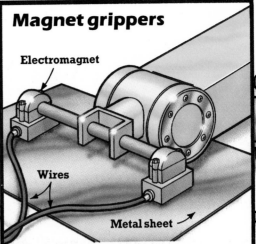

Electromagnet

Wires

Metal sheet

Electric magnets, called electromagnets, are sometimes used as grippers for picking up metal objects. They are connected to a supply of electricity and become magnetic only when the power is switched on by the robot's computer. They lose their magnetism when the power is switched off, and drop what they were holding.

Make your own electromagnet

You can find out how an electromagnet works by making one with a large steel nail, a length of plastic covered wire and a battery.

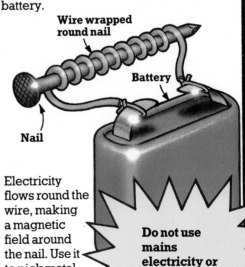

Wire wrapped round nail

Battery

Nail

Electricity flows round the wire, making a magnetic field around the nail. Use it to pick metal things up with the tip of the nail.

Do not use mains electricity or a car battery for this experiment.

Computer control

Computers are programmed to control robots by sending them instructions, which take the form of electrical signals. Computers can also be programmed to react to information from the robot's sensors. These pages explain how an arm robot's computer instructs it to assemble things on a conveyor belt. It also shows how messages from a TV camera sensor make the computer interrupt its instructions to the robot when something goes wrong on the conveyor – when a sleeping cat comes along, for example. All robots are computer-controlled and what they can do depends upon the program used.

Computer messages

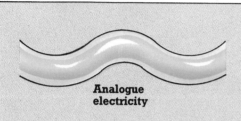

Analogue
electricity

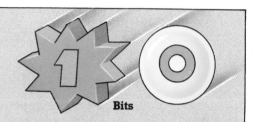

Bits

Most robot motors and sensors work with electricity which is a continuous wave – like the shape a skipping rope makes if two people hold the ends and wiggle the rope up and down. Information in this form is known as "analogue". Computers also use electrical signals but the information is in a different form.

Computers work using individual pulses of electricity called bits. There are two kinds – "no pulse" bits, written as O, which have a very low electric current, and "pulse" bits, written as 1, which have a stronger current. Information in this form is known as "digital" and the 1s and 0s make up a counting system called binary.

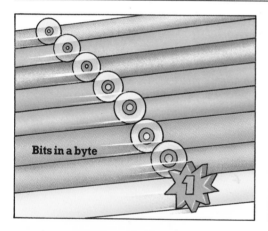

Bits in a byte

The computer is connected to the robot by eight or more wires called the bus. Many computers use groups of eight bits, called bytes, to represent pieces of information. Each byte is an eight-digit code made up of 0s and 1s. Bytes of information from the computer to the motors, and the sensors to the computer, take turns to go along the same bus in opposite directions. This picture shows the eight bits of a byte travelling parallel to each other along a bus.

The digital instructions sent out by the computer go to an interface which has an electronic switch for each of the robot's motors. This picture shows what happens at one switch. The "pulse" bit in the byte turns the switch for one motor either on or off. This allows analogue electricity to flow through the switch and along a wire to the motor. An interface is necessary because the motors do not work with digital pulses.

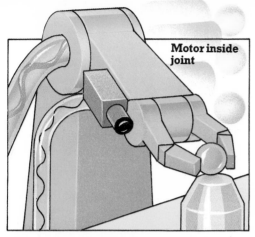

The analogue electricity powers a motor in one of the robot's joints – here it makes the arm go down to assemble two things on the conveyor.

The TV camera sensor on the side of the robot's arm sends pictures, in the form of analogue electricity, of the scene on the conveyor to the computer.

The analogue information from the TV camera is converted into digital information so that the computer can understand it. This is done by an interface, often called an analogue/digital converter.

The computer is programmed to analyse the information from the sensor and to react by switching the robot off if it cannot identify an object on the conveyor, like a sleeping cat.

The computer sends out a byte with a "pulse" bit to the motor switching interface, just as it did to turn the motor on.

The "pulse" bit switches off the analogue electricity flowing through the switch. The motor stops because it has no power.

The whole process takes a split second, so the arm stops moving in time to avoid harming the cat.

Sensors

A robot's computer cannot know what is happening to the robot, or whether the robot has obeyed its instructions, unless it is equipped with sensors. There are two main types – those the robot uses to "touch" with, called contact sensors, and those used to "see" or "hear" with, called non-contact sensors.

Sensors work by sending an electric signal to the computer. The amount of electrical information the sensor sends out, called its output, depends on what the robot's environment does to it. A microphone "ear" would send a lot of information to the computer if someone standing next to the robot screamed, for example. Generally, the more that happens to the sensor, the greater its output.

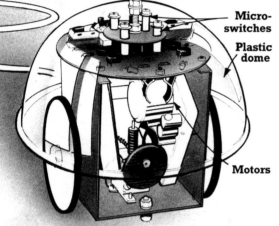

Micro-switches

Plastic dome

Motors

Hebot robot

The micro-robot on the left is equipped with one of the simplest kinds of contact sensor – a switch. There are four switches under the top of the plastic dome, which is loose. When the robot collides with something, the dome touches one of the switches, which sends a signal to the computer to reverse the robot's motors.

Hebot can be programmed to move around like the Turtle and can also be equipped with a pen to draw pictures. The pen can be lifted up and down under the control of the computer.

Touch sensors

Touch, or tactile, sensors tell the computer when, and by how much, the robot is touching something. These sensors are often used on grippers and on the bumpers, or fenders, of mobile robots. The computer needs feedback from these sensors so that it can control the

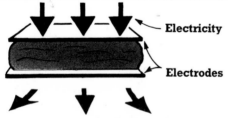

Electricity

Electrodes

robot not to crush whatever it touches. The picture above shows a tactile sensor made from a sandwich of a special foam rubber between two pieces of metal that conduct electricity, called electrodes. When nothing is touching the electrodes, the foam in the middle stops electricity running from one to the other. When the sandwich is squeezed, some of the electricity gets through, and this is converted by the computer into a measurement of pressure.

A light load on the sensor allows a small amount of current to pass from one electrode to another.

A heavy load squeezes the sensor more and lets a lot of electricity pass across the electrodes.

Another touch sensor

This tactile sensor works by using two optical fibres inside a cylinder. Optical fibres are thin tubes of glass used to transmit light. The cylinder has a flexible mirror at one end and two holes in the other. A lamp shines a beam of light down one fibre onto the mirror, which reflects it up the other fibre, and into a photoelectric cell. This detects the amount of reflected light. When the flexible mirror is pressed, less light is reflected into the photoelectric cell. The computer can convert the amount of reflected light into a measurement of pressure on the mirror.

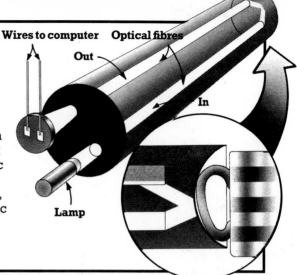

Wires to computer   Optical fibres

Out

In

Lamp

Vision

One of the most powerful non-contact sensors is vision. The picture on the right shows a kind of camera, called a solid state camera, connected to a computer. On the computer screen is the camera's view of a face.

The camera "views" an object with a grid of small, square, light-sensitive cells each of which corresponds to a square on the screen. Each cell is electrically charged. Light areas of an object viewed with the camera make the cells lose a lot of their charge, while dark areas only make them lose a little. The computer converts the charge on each cell into a square of light on the screen.

Solid-state cameras often have over 65,000 cells.

Camera

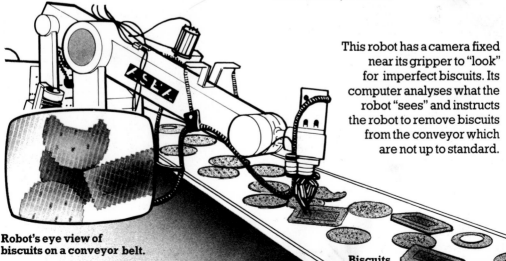

This robot has a camera fixed near its gripper to "look" for imperfect biscuits. Its computer analyses what the robot "sees" and instructs the robot to remove biscuits from the conveyor which are not up to standard.

Robot's eye view of biscuits on a conveyor belt.

Biscuits

79

How a robot knows where it is

These pages explain how two different kinds of sensors are used to make measurements which tell robots where they are. Environmental sensors measure by how far a robot is from something else and positional sensors measure by how much part of a robot has moved.

How a mobile robot knows where it is

A mobile robot has to be equipped with environmental sensors which measure distances between the robot and other objects to find out where it is. One way of doing this is with an ultrasonic sensor which makes "time of flight" recordings. The picture below shows an ultrasonic sensor on an experimental tractor. It works by transmitting a "bleep" of sound and then receiving its echo which bounces back from surrounding objects. The robot's computer works out a distance from the time it takes for the echo to come back.

Puzzle

Sound travels about 330 metres (about 360 yards) in one second. It takes 1½ seconds for the sound to go from this robot's sensor to the tree and back again. How far away is the tree from the robot?

This "bleep" is too high for humans to hear.

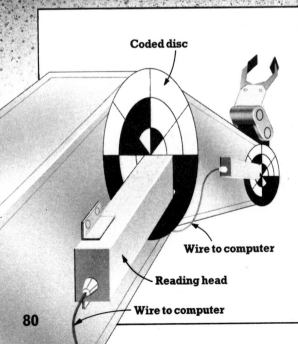

Coded disc

Wire to computer

Reading head

Wire to computer

How robots measure bends

An arm robot's computer needs to know that the robot has carried out its instructions by finding out the position of the arm. This robot has sensors on each of its joints which measure how much it has bent its arm and wrist. The sensor, called an optical position encoder, sends a digital message to the computer which it converts into an angular measurement. The sensor has two parts – a flat disc with marks on it, and a reading head which "reads" the marks. Each segment on the disc represents a number in binary code. The disc is attached to a part of the robot which moves, and the reading head is fixed to a part which stays still. As the robot bends its arm a different number is "read" from the disc and this number is sent to the computer.

How an arm robot knows where it is

Sensors can be fixed to an arm robot to give its computer arm-movement measurements. Some sensors are used to make straight-line measurement, and others to measure angles.

One way of making measurements is with a sensor called an electrical potentiometer. This works like a dimmer switch by varying the amount of electricity passing along a wire. The amount of electricity getting through the wire can be converted into a measurement by connecting it via an interface to the computer.

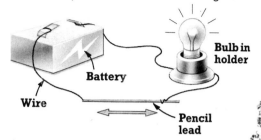

Battery

Bulb in holder

Wire

Pencil lead

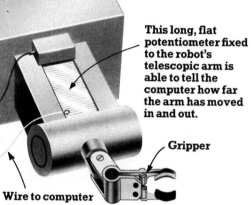

This long, flat potentiometer fixed to the robot's telescopic arm is able to tell the computer how far the arm has moved in and out.

Gripper

Wire to computer

▲
You can test the principle of a potentiometer using a battery, wire, a lamp and a pencil. Carefully split the pencil down the middle, take the lead out and connect everything together as shown. By sliding one end of the wire up and down the pencil lead, you can vary the brightness of the bulb. This happens because the lead resists the flow of electricity.

A special kind of wire which does the same thing as the pencil lead in the experiment shown above, is used in a potentiometer.

Try working out the codes for all the segments.

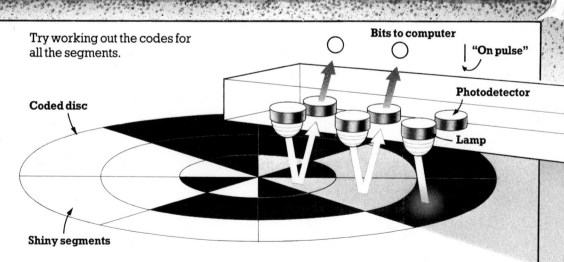

Bits to computer

"On pulse"

Photodetector

Coded disc

Lamp

Shiny segments

The reading head has three pairs of photodetectors and lamps. Shiny white parts on the disc reflect the light into the photodetectors. Shiny parts are registered as 0's, and black parts as 1's. Segment 1, for example, would be "read" as 001. This is called a 3-bit code because the sensor sends three bits to the computer.

Cybernetics

Cybernetics is the science of control and communication in both machines and living organisms. The word comes from a Greek word meaning "steersman". It is particularly concerned with things which are self-controlling, or adaptive. An adaptive system alters its behaviour because of changes in its environment. For example, George, an automatic pilot used in aeroplanes, alters the course of the plane as a result of changes in the wind speed.

Artificial intelligence

A closely related field to cybernetics is artificial intelligence (AI) which is about making machines do intelligent things. Machines have to be able to "think" to do something intelligent, but experts disagree about what this means. There are some who believe that a machine which "learns" from past experience, or responds to things happening to it, like George, can be called a "thinking" machine. Others argue that for machines to think they must have feelings and want to do things. This would mean that a "thinking" robot, for instance, would have to want to pack boxes because it enjoyed its work.

Clever machines

Computers are the cleverest machines available because by ingenious programming they can be made to simulate, or mimic, intelligent human activity, such as the processing of visual information and speech. Computers can then be used to control other machines, like robots, to make them behave "intelligently".

"Intelligent" computer

There are two basic ways of programming a computer. Algorithmic programs – often used for robots – work by considering all the possible alternatives in a situation. Heuristic programs are "cleverer" because they take short-cuts to decisions by remembering from past experience the best way to solve a problem. A chess-playing robot computer could work out the best moves by being given the rules of the game, for example. AI programs are often heuristic.

Speech recognition

Computer programs are being developed to give robots the ability to recognize spoken commands, using a microphone as an electronic "ear". The average adult knows thousands of words, so it would take a computer with a massive memory to understand even a tiny fraction of them. The computer also has to take into account the different ways that people speak. It is much simpler to program the computer to recognize only a short list of words, spoken by one person, which are needed for the robot's job.

How computers recognize words

1. Each word makes wave-like patterns of sound that are converted by a microphone into electricity. The waves vary according to the different sounds in a word.

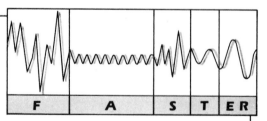

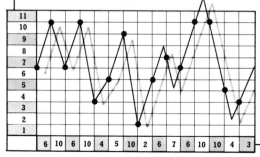

| 6 | 10 | 6 | 10 | 4 | 5 | 10 | 2 | 6 | 7 | 6 | 10 | 10 | 4 | 3 |

2. The height of the wave, which is an electrical voltage, is measured many times a second. These measurements are recorded as a sequence of numbers, and then turned into a digital code of "pulse" and "no pulse" bits which the computer can then use to identify the word. The picture on the left shows how a word like "faster" would look to the computer.

Vision

Robots are increasingly being equipped with machine vision which allows them to "see" and behave "intelligently". The intelligent part of this is not the TV camera eye, the computer brain, or the robot, but the computer program. This analyses and interprets what the "eye" sees – something which is extremely complicated. Humans are very selective in what they actually see, and this is difficult to simulate with a computer. For example, if you look carefully at this picture you will be able to choose whether you see either a vase or two faces. Machine vision could not do this.

How robots recognize things

A machine vision system can be programmed to recognize one or more objects. This shows how an object in a pile can be recognized, so that a vision system can tell a robot how to pick it up correctly for packing in a box.

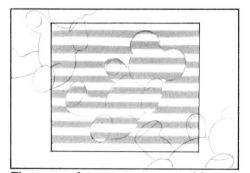

The system focuses on one part of the pile and projects stripes of light over it to judge how far away it is. This information is sent to the robot's computer.

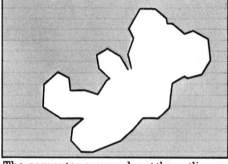

The computer can work out the outline of one bear from the breaks in the stripes of light. It is programmed only to identify the outline of bears and will not recognize anything else.

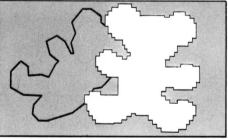

By comparing this outline with views of the bear stored in its memory, the computer can work out the position of the bear in the pile. This information is then sent to the robot in the form of instructions to its motors.

The computer controls the robot to pick the bear up without damaging it or any of the other bears. It then turns the bear the right way round for packing. This sequence is repeated for all the bears.

Latest developments

Robotics is a fast-moving and exciting subject with many research projects going on around the world. More and more arm robots are being used in factories along with other automatic machines. Robots are also being made more "intelligent" by using more and better sensors together with clever computer programs for their control. This means mobile and other kinds of robots may soon become more familiar – perhaps in the home as robot "servants" and in factories too. Robots are also becoming cheaper – a micro-robot costs about the same as some home computers. Some of the latest developments are shown here.

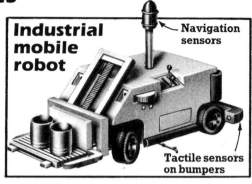

Industrial mobile robot

Navigation sensors

Tactile sensors on bumpers

This is a driverless forklift truck which will be used in an automated warehouse or factory. It has an on-board computer and power supply and uses sensors to navigate.

Nuclear reactor robot

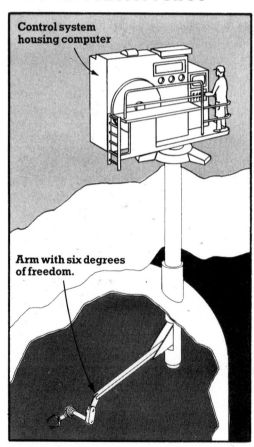

Control system housing computer

Arm with six degrees of freedom.

This arm robot is designed to be used in the core of a nuclear reactor. The arm is suspended from a long hollow chain. Control cables for the arm pass through the chain.

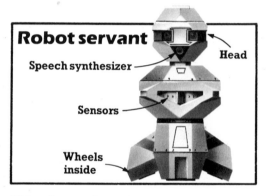

Robot servant

Head

Speech synthesizer

Sensors

Wheels inside

This robot can be programmed to do things like serve drinks at a party and speak to guests with its synthesized voice. Others are being made which do housework.

Robot metro

A completely automatic robot train has been built in Lille, France. The trains are computer-controlled to switch between tracks and are programmed to stop automatically at stations.

Robot computer assistant

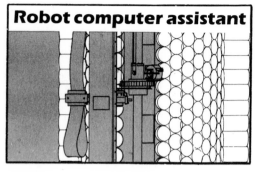

This arm robot goes up and down in a honeycomb storage cell to find special cartridges containing computer data. It delivers the cartridges to the computer and replaces them after use.

Two-armed robot

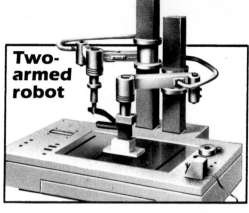

Yes-Man is designed to work alongside humans on a production line. Its arms allow it to do complex assembly work – it can even do two things at once. The base contains control microcomputers.

Walking robot

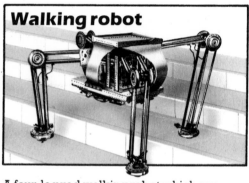

A four-legged walking robot which can climb stairs has been built by Japanese scientists. Other researchers are trying out six- and eight-legged designs which walk like insects.

Modular arm robot

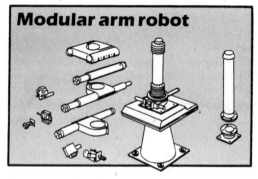

Some arm robots are being made in modules – small units, such as arm, wrist, base and so on – that can be combined in different ways to make a robot suitable for a particular job.

Robot cleaning machine

Twin scrubbing brushes

A free-roving, industrial floor-scrubbing robot is being developed. As well as navigation sensors, it will probably have a sensor to detect when the water becomes dirty.

Android

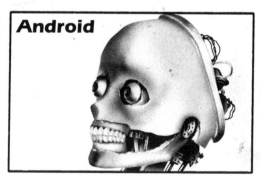

Androids – robots which look and act like humans – are being made, mostly for exhibitions and shop displays. This one is powered by electric motors and hydraulic pistons.

85

Build your own micro-robot

The next nine pages show how to build a computer-controlled micro-robot. You need a computer with a parallel input/output port to control the robot (see page 94 to find out if your computer is suitable). The project gives step by step instructions on how to make an electronic interface circuit to connect the robot to a computer, with hints on soldering and components. A computer program is included which will control the robot to move like a Turtle or a Bigtrak (see page 64).

The robot is made using a flat base-board with two motors, two gearboxes and two wheels mounted on it. It also has a small wheel at the back which stops the robot from tipping up. The wheels are driven by separate motors, via gearboxes which reduce the speed of the motors. The computer steers the robot by controlling the direction of the two motors. See page 54 to see how this works. You could put a cardboard body over the base, and this can be any shape you like. Page 49 shows a picture of a home-made, robot mouse for example.

The robot can be made to turn left and right, and to go forwards and backwards. The computer program in this project lets you give the robot a sequence of instructions to move it in any direction you like. By attaching a pen to the robot with tape, you can make it draw pictures.

The electronic part of this project is not easy to build. A single faulty component or a tiny mistake could prevent the robot from working. The robot itself can be built using parts from a construction kit, such as Fischertechnic. The robot below is made in this way, but other methods are suggested. The project may be quite expensive, depending on whether you already have a construction kit. It is a good idea to work out the cost of all the components before starting.

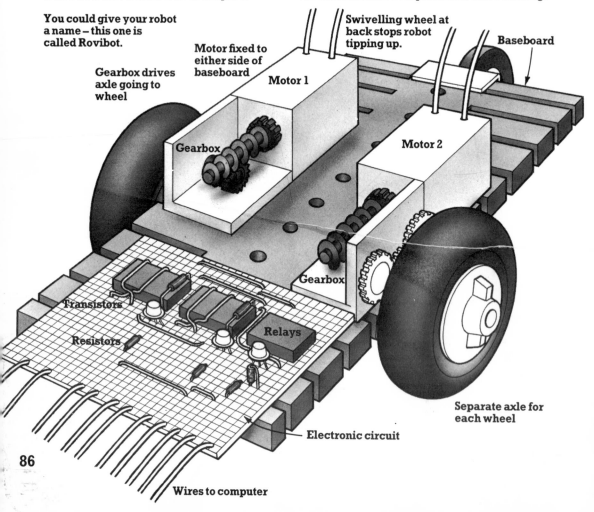

You could give your robot a name – this one is called Rovibot.

Motor fixed to either side of baseboard

Gearbox drives axle going to wheel

Swivelling wheel at back stops robot tipping up.

Baseboard

Motor 1

Motor 2

Gearbox

Gearbox

Transistors

Resistors

Relays

Separate axle for each wheel

Electronic circuit

Wires to computer

86

Components for the project

You can buy components in an electronic components shop, or you can buy a mail order kit of either the electronic or the mechanical parts for the project from a supplier listed on page 94. Ask in your local TV repair shop if you are not sure where the nearest component shop is. It is a good idea to take this book with you.

Parts for robot

2 × motors with a voltage range between 3V-12V (construction kit motors, like Fischertechnic, are ideal but you could also use motors from an old battery-powered toy car, or buy motors from a model shop).
2 × gearboxes which match the motors (i.e. if you use Fischertechnic motors you will need the same make of gearbox).
2 × wheels and axles (make sure they will fit the gearbox).
1 × small swivelling wheel.
Baseplate (use a piece of plywood about 100mm × 200mm × 10mm if you do not have a construction kit).

Parts for electronic circuit

2 × double-pole changeover relays, coil voltage 6V d.c., coil resistance greater than 50Ω (250Ω is best), suitable for 0.1 inch pitch Veroboard.
1 × single-pole relay with the same specifications as above (see notes on relays on page 88).
3 × transistors 2N222A, BC107 or BC108 or any NPN transistor with a current gain (HFE factor) greater than 100.
3 × 2.2K Ω resistors
3 × diodes IN4001, IN4002 or IN4003. (Do not use Zener diodes).
Veroboard with copper strips, size 0.1 inch pitch, 30 tracks × 26 holes or Prototype board, which you do not need to solder.

Other things you need

Soldering iron, cored solder, wire cutters, wire strippers, thin-nosed pliers, 22m of thin electric wire ("bell wire" or stranded wire is best), electrical tape, dress-maker's pins, pencils, tracing paper, paper glue, damp sponge,
4.5mm twist drill.

Power supply

Use battery or transformer power supply. DO NOT use car batteries or mains electricity as this is very dangerous. The power supply must match the voltage of the motors you use (i.e. 6V motors need a 6V battery or a 6V transformer).

About the electronic components

The electronic components you buy may not look the same as the ones drawn in this book. Some components MUST be connected a certain way round. Many components have marks or tags on them to identify particular legs, others come with diagrams. Some diagrams are labelled "pin view", which means you have to look at the component upside down, with its pins facing you, to identify them.

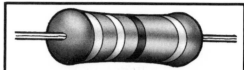

Resistors: These are used to reduce the amount of current in a circuit. It does not matter which way round they go. Colour coded stripes on the resistor show how many ohms (written Ω or KΩ for 1,000 ohms) it is.

Stripe this end

Diodes: These allow current to flow in one direction only – a bit like a one way street for electricity. Diodes only work one way round, so they have a stripe at one end to identify which way they should go.

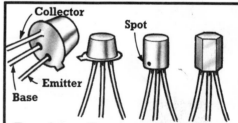

Collector
Spot
Emitter
Base

Transistors: Transistors are used in this project as switches to turn current on and off. They have three legs, a "collector", an "emitter" and a "base", and they must be connected up the right way. The centre leg is usually the base and the emitter is usually next to a tag, or other mark, on the case of the transistor. The transistors in this project are switched on and off by the computer.

Relays

Relays are electronic switches, activated by an electromagnet. Two types are used in the project – a single-pole relay with one switch inside, and a double-pole relay with two switches inside. When the electromagnet is off, the switch, or switches, stay in one position. When the electromagnet is on, the magnetic field pushes the switch into another position. The electromagnets in the relays used in this project are switched on and off by transistors.

It is not usually possible to see how to connect a relay by looking at the case or the pins underneath. Ask for a circuit diagram showing the inside. Pin connections vary according to manufacturer and type of relay. These pictures show the type used in this project and their circuits. Look carefully at the circuit diagram for your relays and substitute the pin numbers with those used below. Unless you do this, your relay may not match the pin numbers used in the instructions for the circuit.

Sub-miniature change-over relays

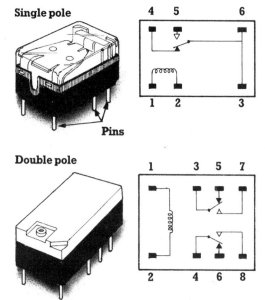

Single pole

Pins

Double pole

If the diagram with your relay says "pin view", make sure you identify the pins with them facing you.

Check point

The instructions on this project are given for sub-miniature relays with the pins in the same positions as those shown on the guide below, as well as the same circuit inside. Check that the pins on your relay are in the right positions by putting them over the guides to see if they line up.

Single pole	Double pole
●● ●	● ● ●
●● ●	● ● ●

If your relay does not line up with these guides, this is what to do:
Either: Turn the relay on its back and solder a piece of tinned wire (see hints on soldering on page 89) about 75mm long to each leg. Look carefully at the circuit diagram for your relay and substitute its pin numbers for those shown in the project. You can then solder the wires into the Veroboard instead of the pins.
Or: Look at the circuit diagram at the end of the project and work out a new circuit to suit the layout of the pins on your relay by looking at the diagram on page 94.

Veroboard

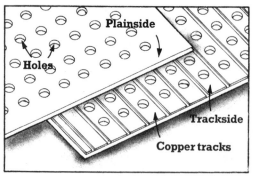

A special board, called Veroboard, is used to connect the electronic components together. This has rows of holes in it, with copper strips on the back linking them together. You push the legs of the components through the holes and solder them to this copper track. Electric current can then flow along the track between the components. Make sure the components do not touch each other on the Veroboard, especially the transistors.

Hints on soldering

Soldering is a way of joining two pieces of metal together, using another metal called solder, melted with a soldering iron. The picture on the left shows the things you need. Make sure the soldering iron is kept propped up when you are not using it so as not to burn anything.

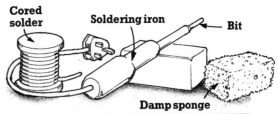

Cored solder   Soldering iron   Bit

Damp sponge

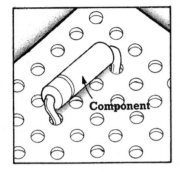

1. Push the legs of the components through the holes on the plainside of the Veroboard.

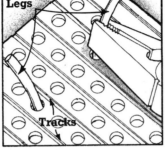

Legs   Tracks

2. Turn the Veroboard over, and bend the legs out slightly, using the pliers.

3. Wipe the bit on the damp sponge to remove old solder.

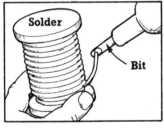

Solder   Bit

4. Touch the bit with solder so that a drop clings to it to "wet" it. This is called "wetting" the bit.

Remove any solder between tracks by running the hot bit along in the groove.

5. Carefully touch the bit on one side of the leg where it touches the track, while at the same time touching the solder on the other side of the leg. Hold them there for about one second until a small blob of solder flows around the leg. Let the joint cool for a few seconds while the solder hardens.

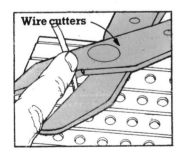

Wire cutters

6. Trim the legs close to the solder with wire cutters. Hold the board away from your face and put your finger on the leg to stop it flying up in the air.

Bit

Do not forget to unplug the soldering iron when finished.

Pliers

Wires: The ends of pieces of wire should be covered with solder. This is called "tinning". Stroke the wire quickly with the bit and the solder at the same time until the wire is lightly coated with solder. Tinning is done to get a good connection when soldering. It also holds together the strands of stranded wire to stop them unwinding. Tin the area of wire you have stripped.

Motor control circuit

The motor control circuit enables the computer to switch both motors on or off, or to control each motor independently to go forwards or reverse. The instructions have to be followed very accurately for the circuit to work.

Drill bit

Guide ▽

← **Tracks run horizontally** →

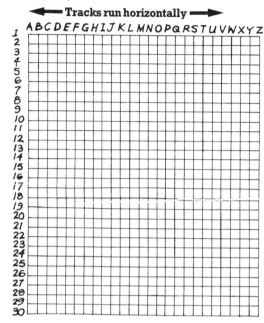

A B C D E F G H I J K L M N O P Q R S T U V W X Y Z

(rows 1–30)

1. Photocopy or trace the positioning guide above, then cut it out.

2. Put a dab of glue under each corner of the guide.

3. Place the guide on the plainside of the Veroboard by pushing a pin through holes A1 and Z30 to help line up the guide with the holes and tracks of the Veroboard.

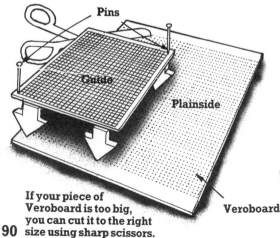

Pins

Guide

Plainside

If your piece of Veroboard is too big, you can cut it to the right size using sharp scissors.

Veroboard

4. Cut the track with a 4.5mm drill bit at holes H2, H3, H7, H10, H13, H15, H17, H20, H23, H25, H27, Q4, Q9, Q19. Hold the bit in your fingers and turn it to remove all the copper from the track.

5. Place a single-pole relay on the Veroboard with the pins in these holes:
Pin 1: J2
Pin 2: J3
Pin 3: J7
Pin 4: G2
Pin 5: G3
Pin 6: G7
Solder each pin, taking care not to join the tracks with solder.

6. Place a double-pole relay on the Veroboard in these holes and solder each pin.
Pin 1: G10
Pin 2: J10
Pin 3: G13
Pin 4: J13
Pin 5: G15
Pin 6: J15
Pin 7: G17
Pin 8: J17

7.
Place a double-pole relay on the Veroboard in these holes and solder each pin:
Pin 1: G20
Pin 2: J20
Pin 3: G23
Pin 4: J23
Pin 5: G25
Pin 6: J25
Pin 7: G27
Pin 8: J27

Relay with wires soldered to pins

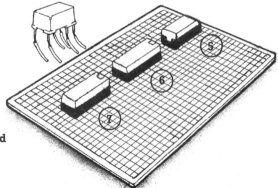

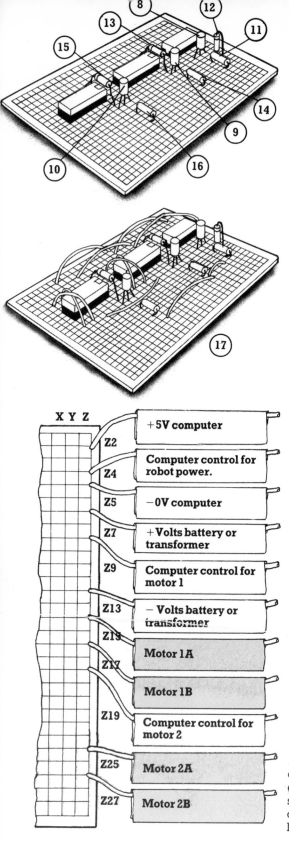

X	Y	Z			
			+5V computer		
		Z2			
			Computer control for robot power.		
		Z4			
		Z5	−0V computer		
		Z7	+Volts battery or transformer		
		Z9	Computer control for motor 1		
		Z13	− Volts battery or transformer		
		Z15			
			Motor 1A		
		Z17			
			Motor 1B		
		Z19	Computer control for motor 2		
		Z25	Motor 2A		
		Z27	Motor 2B		

8. Solder the collector leg of a transistor in hole M3, the base leg in hole M4 and the emitter leg in hole M5.

9. Solder the emitter leg of a transistor in hole M8, the base leg in hole M9 and the collector leg in hole M10.

10. Solder the emitter leg of a transistor in hole M18, the base leg in hole M19 and the collector leg in hole M20.

11. Solder a resistor with one leg in hole P4 and the other in hole S4.

12. Solder a diode with the leg nearest the striped end in hole P2 and the other in hole P3.

13. Solder a diode with the leg nearest the striped end in hole E10 and other leg in hole L10.

14. Solder a resistor with one leg in hole P9 and the other in hole S9.

15. Solder a diode with the leg nearest the striped end in hole E20, and the other in hole L20.

16. Solder a resistor with one leg in hole P19 and the other in hole S19.

17. Cut 11 lengths of wire about 100mm long. Strip each end about 10mm. Tin both ends of each wire. Then loop one wire between each of the following pairs of holes and solder them into place as you go:

L2 and D10, C2 and C13, B13 and B23, C10 and C20, E15 and L17, E17 and L15, E25 and L27, E27 and L25, T5 and T8, U8 and U18, M13 and M23.

18. Cut 7 lengths of wire about 3m long. Strip each end about 10mm and tin one end. Label each wire with a piece of tape as shown in the white labels on the left. Label the other end of each wire with the same label. Solder the tinned end of each wire into the holes shown on the left. Label each wire as you go, otherwise you might get muddled up.

19. Cut 4 lengths of wire about 250mm long. Strip each end about 10mm and tin one end. Label each wire with a piece of tape, as shown in the shaded labels on the left. Solder the tinned end of each wire into the holes shown next to these labels.

How to connect circuit to computer, motors and power

Computer: Connect circuit to computer's parallel input/output port by the wires soldered at step 18 in the instructions. You will probably need to buy an edge connector to plug into the port. You can get these from component or computer shops. Use computer's handbook to identify pins in the port, and connect up to wires shown in white spaces in the chart below.

Motors: Connect wires soldered at step 19 in the instructions to the terminals of the motors, as shown in shaded spaces in the chart.

Power supply: Connect the last two wires labelled in the chart to the + and − terminals of your battery or transformer.

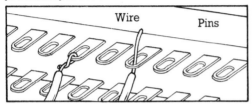

Wire   Pins

Push the wires through the holes in the pins on the edge connector and twist them round, making sure that the wires do not touch each other. Do not solder.

Wire label	Connection
+5V computer	5 volt pin of user port
−0V computer	0 volt pin of user port
Computer control for motor 1	PB2 pin of user port
Computer control for motor 2	PB0 pin of user port
Computer control for robot power	PB1 pin of user port
Motor 1A	Right hand terminal of motor 1
Motor 1B	Left hand terminal of motor 1
Motor 2A	Right hand terminal of motor 2
Motor 2B	Left hand terminal of motor 2
+volts battery/transformer	+ volt terminal of battery or transformer
−volts battery/transformer	− volt terminal of battery or transformer

Computer program

The computer program opposite allows the robot to go forwards, backwards, left or right, so many units at a time. You will have to experiment to find out how far each unit is because it depends on the number you set in line 650 of the program. The larger the number, the further each unit will make the robot go. This menu will appear on the screen once you have entered the program.

1. Tell me what to do
2. Go
3. Clear memory

If you press 1, then RETURN, you can give the robot any of these instructions: **Forwards:** Press F, then RETURN, then a number, then RETURN. Pressing F RETURN 6 RETURN will make the robot ready to go forward 6 units, for example.
Backwards: Press B, then RETURN, then a number, then RETURN.
Left: Press L, then RETURN, then a number, then RETURN.
Right: Press R, then RETURN, then a number, then RETURN.
Stop: Press S and program will go back to the menu.

To make the robot carry out your instructions, press 2, then RETURN. You can give it a sequence of instructions, for example, forwards 5, left 3, forwards 6, back 2 and so on. After pressing 2 to make the robot go, the instructions will be displayed on the screen as the robot moves. To give the robot new instructions, press 3, then RETURN.

Adjusting the program

Before entering the program in your computer you will need to do some tests to see what numbers to enter in lines 580, 590, 600, 610, 690 and 740.
1. Connect up as shown on this page.
2. Type this program into your computer.

```
10 ?&FE62=7
20 LET DL=&FE60
30 INPUT P
40 ?DL=P
```

3. Type the numbers 0 to 7 one at a time. Look to see which direction the robot's motors run in response to each number. Write the number which makes the motors run in the correct direction into the program, at the lines shown below.
580 – Both motors forward
590 – Both motors backwards
600 – Motor 1 forwards, motor 2 backwards.
610 – Motor 1 backwards, motor 2 forwards
690 and 740 – both motors off

```
◇▲  10 ?&FE62=7
◇▲  20 LET OL=&FE60
    30 DIM D(20)
    40 DIM M$(20)
    50 GOSUB 550
▲   60 CLS
    70 PRINT "ROBOT CONTROL"
    80 PRINT
    90 PRINT "1. TELL ME WHAT TO DO"
   100 PRINT "2. GO"
   110 PRINT "3. CLEAR MEMORY"
   120 PRINT
   130 PRINT "TYPE NUMBER"
   140 INPUT C
   150 IF C<1 OR C>3 THEN GOTO 130
◇  160 ON C GOSUB 180,440,550
   170 GOTO 60
   180 LET PC=PS
▲  190 CLS
   200 IF PC=20 THEN GOTO 390
   210 PRINT
   220 PRINT "INPUT STEP ";PC
   230 PRINT "DIRECTION THEN TIME"
   240 INPUT M$(PC)
   250 IF M$(PC)="S" THEN GOTO 410
   260 INPUT D(PC)
   270 LET P=999
   280 GOSUB 580
   290 IF P<>999 AND D(PC)>0 THEN GOTO 320
   300 PRINT "WRONG COMMAND"
   310 GOTO 220
   320 GOSUB 630
▲  330 CLS
   340 FOR I=1 TO PC
   350 PRINT "STEP ";I;": ";M$(I);" ";D(I)
   360 NEXT I
   370 LET PC=PC+1
   380 GOTO 200
   390 PRINT "NO MORE STEPS"
   400 LET M$(PC)="S"
   410 LET PS=PC
   420 GOSUB 710
   430 RETURN
▲  440 CLS
   450 LET PC=1
   460 PRINT "STEP ";PC;": ";M$(PC);" ";D(PC)
   470 IF M$(PC)="S" THEN GOTO 520
   480 GOSUB 580
   490 GOSUB 630
   500 LET PC=PC+1
   510 GOTO 460
   520 PRINT "END OF INSTRUCTIONS"
   530 GOSUB 710
   540 RETURN
   550 LET M$(1)="S"
   560 LET PS=1
   570 RETURN
   580 IF M$(PC)="F" THEN LET P=1
   590 IF M$(PC)="B" THEN LET P=2
   600 IF M$(PC)="R" THEN LET P=0
   610 IF M$(PC)="L" THEN LET P=3
   620 RETURN
◇▲ 630 ?OL=P
   640 FOR J=1 TO D(PC)
   650 FOR L=1 TO 100
   660 NEXT L
◇▲ 670 IF INKEY$(0)="S" THEN GOTO 740
   680 NEXT J
◇▲ 690 ?OL=4
   700 RETURN
   710 PRINT "PRESS RETURN FOR MENU"
   720 INPUT Z$
   730 RETURN
◇▲ 740 ?OL=4
   750 STOP
```

Arranges output and makes space for instructions to the robot. — *Input instructions*

Prints menu on the screen.

Goes to part of the program that organizes instructions to the robot.

Lets you give the robot instructions. If you run out of memory for instructions, the program returns you to STOP. — *Instructions*

Analyses the instructions and carries them out as long as they are valid commands.

Lists instructions given so far on the screen.

Goes back for the next instruction to the robot.

If the last instruction is stop, program goes back to the menu.

Carries out instructions to the robot after pressing 2. — *Go*

If you press 3, the program clears the last set of instructions to the robot. — *Clear*

Looks at the instruction and decides what number to output. — *Analyse*

Makes robot move according to the instructions given to it. — *Move*

Waits for RETURN to be pressed. — *Wait*

Stops everything if you press S.

93

Changes for other computers

▲ VIC 20   ◇ ZX81 (Timex 1000)

◇10 DELETE
▲ 10 POKE 37138,7
◇20 LET OL=NUMBER OF MEMORY LOCATION FOR OUTPUT
▲ 20 LET OL=37136
▲ 60,190,330,440 PRINT CHR$(147)

◇ 160 GOSUB 180*(C=1)+440*(C=2)+550*(C=3)
◇▲ 630 POKE OL,P
◇ 670 IF INKEY$="S" THEN GOTO 740
▲ 670 GET A$:IF A$="S" THEN GOTO 740
◇▲ 690,740 POKE OL,P

Wiring diagram

Look at the diagram and work out a new circuit if your relays do not suit the instructions.

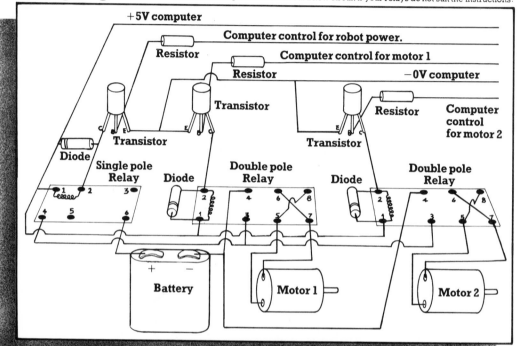

Computers you can use with this project

BBC Model B
Commodore VIC 20
*Sinclair ZX81 (Timex 1000)
*Sinclair Spectrum (Timex 2000)
*You need a special interface for these computers. You can buy one by mail order from this company.
Colne Robotics Co Ltd, Beaufort Road, off Richmond Road, East Twickenham, Middlesex, TW1 2PQ, England.
Or you can get a kit (not easy to assemble) from: Powertran Cybernetics, Portway Industrial Estate, Andover, Hampshire, England.
Also look in computer magazines for advertisements

Complete kit of parts for robot and circuit

You can buy a kit of parts by mail order from: Bluepond Electronics, Alpha Road, Crawley, Sussex, England.
Send a stamped addressed envelope to these companies for details of their products.

What to do if the robot does not work

Carefully check that you have all the components in the correct place and resolder any which look loose. Make sure that all the wires are connected properly and that they don't touch each other. Check you have good batteries and the cut-out switch if you are using a transformer. If the robot still does not work, get someone else to look at it, as it is easy to miss something. Make sure that your motors work by connecting them directly to a suitable battery. If you still cannot get the circuit to work pack it carefully (with enough stamps for return postage) and send to:

Electronics Advisor,
Usborne Publishing,
20 Garrick Street,
London, WC2E 9BJ.

Robot words

Android: A kind of robot made to look human.

Artificial Intelligence: The study of making machines do "intelligent things". Experts disagree on a precise definition of what counts as intelligence or intelligent behaviour.

Degrees of freedom: A technical term used to describe the different directions an arm robot can move. Usually, the more joints a robot has in its arm, the more degrees of freedom it has.

Feedback: Information about the robot or its surroundings that a computer gets from sensors on the robot.

Gears: These reduce or increase the speed of a motor. They are used between a motor and the part of a robot that it drives.

Gripper: The mechanism fixed to an arm robot's wrist to hold things. Sometimes called an end effector.

Hydraulic system: A device using a special oil in pipes and cylinders to drive mechanical parts of a robot. Often used on arm robots.

Interface: Used between a robot and its computer to convert electrical signals from the computer into instructions from the robot and vice versa.

Lead-through programming: A way of teaching a robot by guiding it through the movements needed to do a job.

LOGO: A computer language often used to program robots which draw, like the Turtle.

Machine vision: A computer-controlled device used to give robots a primitive kind of sight.

Navigation: How a computer uses information from a mobile robot's sensors to get the robot from one place to another without bumping into anything.

Odometer: A sensor that measures the distance travelled by a wheeled vehicle.

Photoelectric cell: An electronic device which detects light. These are often used as part of a sensor on robots.

Pitch: The name for the up and down movement in a robot's wrist, which is like the movement made when using a lever.

Pneumatic system: A device powered by air or another gas to operate a mechanical part of a robot – often the gripper.

Port: The socket on a computer where interfaces and other kinds of electronic equipment are plugged in.

Program: A sequence of instructions given to a computer that controls everything the robot does.

Robot: A computer-controlled machine which can be programmed to do different kinds of things. Experts do not agree on an exact definition of a robot.

Roll: A name for the movement in a robot's wrist which goes from side to side like rocking a boat.

Sensor: A device which gives a robot's computer information either about the robot or its surroundings.

Sonar sensor: Often used for navigation, these sensors emit a sound and then "listen" for an echo to bounce back from obstacles. Distances are calculated by the time taken for the sound to return.

Speech synthesizer: An electronic device, often a chip, which can be programmed to produce words and sentences through a loudspeaker. Each word is broken down into small units of sound, which are then reproduced digitally.

Transformer: An electronic device which converts mains electricity into low voltage suitable for powering things like micro-robots and train sets.

Turtle: A wheeled micro-robot programmed to move about and draw, using a computer language called LOGO.

Working envelope: The area of space that an arm robot is able to reach.

Yaw: The name given to the left and right movement in a robot's wrist – similar to the movement made steering a bicycle.

Index

The publishers would like to thank the following for their help:
Artur Fischer (UK) Ltd.
Andrew Lennard, Colne Robotics Co. Ltd.
John Jessop, Jessop Microelectronics Ltd.
Peter Mathews, Upperdata Ltd.

Dr George Russell, Heriot-Watt University.
Milton Bradley Europe.
Economatics Ltd.

LASERS

Lynn Myring and Maurice Kimmitt

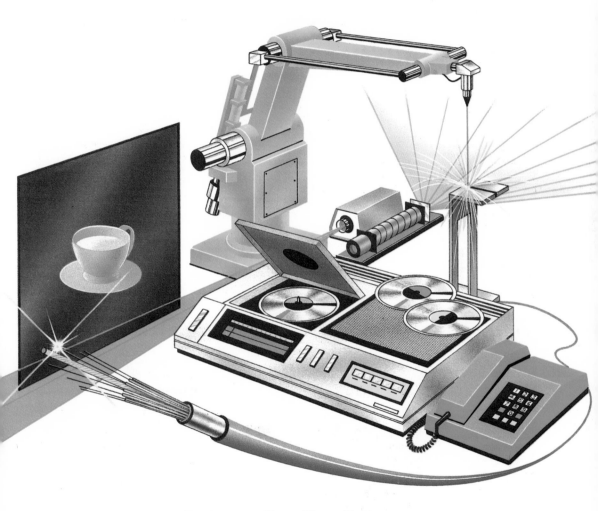

Assistant editor   Tony Potter

Designed by Richard Lee, Roger Boffey, Roger Priddy, Gerry Downes

Illustrated by Chris Lyon, Martin Newton,
Jeremy Gower, Simon Roulstone, Kai Choi,
Hussein Hussein, Graham Round

Contents

About lasers

This part of the book explains what lasers are and how they work, looking at the different kinds and showing how they are used. A laser is a device which produces beams of a special kind of light – laser light. A laser beam looks like a straight, almost solid, yet transparent rod of intense light. It

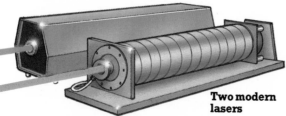

Two modern lasers

is just light, but is quite different from ordinary light in several ways, which are outlined on this page and explained later in this section.

A laser beam is light of only one colour; ordinary "white" light is many colours mixed together. Ordinary light spreads out in all directions; laser beams stay almost parallel. The lightwaves in a laser beam are in step with each other and work together to make the beam concentrated and very bright; ordinary light waves are not in step. In fact laser light is the brightest, most intense light known – even brighter than the sun.

The first laser

The theory of laser light was first suggested in 1957 by two American scientists, Charles Townes and Arthur Schawlow, but the first laser was not actually made until 1960. It was built by another American scientist, Theodore Maiman. This first laser was made from a rod of synthetic ruby and it created a laser beam when an intense flash of ordinary light was shone on it. Later research has shown that many materials, not just ruby, can be made to give off laser light – and that they can be stimulated in other ways as well as by light. Many different kinds of laser have been built and new kinds are being tried all the time. They all produce slightly different beams and so are useful for many varied jobs.

In its early days the laser was described as a solution looking for a problem. Scientists knew that it had many useful properties – beams were powerful enough to melt metals, yet could be focused to precise points for delicate work.

Now there are many thousands of problems which lasers are helping to solve. Lasers are used to cut, weld, engrave and make all kinds of things, from cars to clothing, from microchips to newspapers. Beams help build vertical skyscrapers and align underground pipes; they measure distances both microscopic and vast.

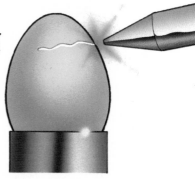

Laser delicately cutting eggshell

Lasers also carry phone calls and TV pictures over long distances, play video discs and scan bar codes in supermarkets. Doctors also use lasers for "bloodless surgery" which is less painful for the patient and easier for the surgeon. The laser has often proved to be better than traditional methods in all of these jobs, and many more. The development of the laser also gave scientists and artists the tool they needed to make amazing 3D photographs called holograms. The beams themselves are so beautiful that they are even used for special light shows and in concerts and discos.

Some everyday things processed by laser beams

Light and laser light

A laser produces light, but it is organized in a different way to the ordinary light of lamps and the Sun. Laser beams are different in several ways and it is these differences which make them special and useful for so many jobs.

These two pages look at both laser and ordinary light, explaining what they are and illustrating their differences and similarities.

Light waves

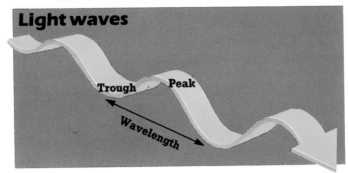

Light travels as a continuous stream of waves. The high points of a wave are called peaks, the low points troughs. Light is measured in two ways: by wavelength (the distance between two peaks) and by frequency (the number of waves a second).

Colour

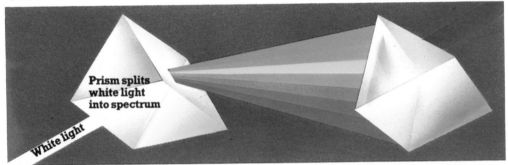

rdinary "white" light is actually a mixture f different colours muddled together. You can use a prism to split up white light to see these colours. They fall into bands of red, orange, yellow, green, blue, indigo and violet, called a spectrum. Each colour is light of a particular wavelength; violet has a short wavelength, red a long one and the others are in between.

One colour and direction

A red light bulb produces light of one colour but it is really a mixture of all the different wavelengths that make various reds, and probably some orange, yellow and other colours too. Laser beams are made up of light waves of identical wavelength, so they are truly just one colour or "monochromatic".

The light waves in a beam of ordinary light spread out in all directions, so the beam quickly fades as it travels. In a laser beam the light waves all travel in the same direction, forming a straight, nearly parallel "rod" of concentrated light which keeps its intensity, even over long distances.

Light waves in step

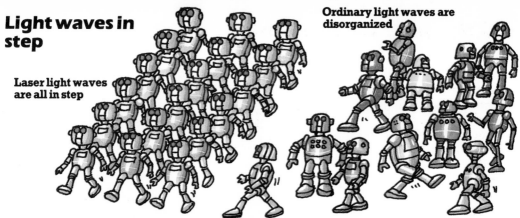

Laser light waves are all in step

Ordinary light waves are disorganized

Not only are the light waves in a laser beam all identical in wavelength and frequency, they are all in step with each other – rather like people marching. This is called being in phase. Light which is in phase is known as "coherent" light – lasers are the only source of coherent light. In ordinary light the waves are all different and so are out of phase – like a crowd wandering around a fair. This is known as "incoherent" light.

Photons

Blue, short-wavelength, high energy photons

Yellow, medium length and medium energy photons

Red, long wave, low energy photons

Light waves consist of packets of energy called photons. Each photon belonging to a particular wavelength has the same energy. But, photons of different wavelengths (colours) have different energies – the longer the wavelength, the lower the energy. So red is lower energy light than violet, with the others in between.

Laser speckle

A curious thing about laser light is that it looks sparkling and speckled with out-of-focus, tiny bright and dark spots. This is caused by the light waves in the beam bouncing off a surface. Even the most flat looking surface is a mountainous landscape when seen through a microscope. These hills and valleys put some of the coherent light waves out of step with each other. When the peaks of one wave meet with the troughs of another wave, they cancel each other out, making what you see as a tiny spot of dark. When the peaks of both meet, they add together to form what you see as a bright sparkle.

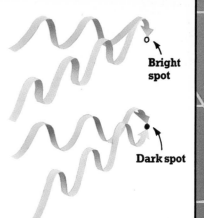

Bright spot

Dark spot

101

How lasers work

The name "laser" actually describes how a laser beam is made. The word is made up from the first letters of the phrase "Light Amplification by Stimulated Emission of Radiation". This phrase describes what happens inside a laser, and the process is illustrated and explained below.

A laser is a device made out of a substance that will give off light when excited by a source of energy. There are many kinds of laser, as you will see over the page, but the basic process of making a laser beam is the same for all of them. It is explained here using a gas laser, the most common kind, as an example.

Inside a laser

This is a simplified pictured of a gas laser, drawn so that you can see inside. There is a glass tube filled with gas and this is stimulated by an electric current going through it.

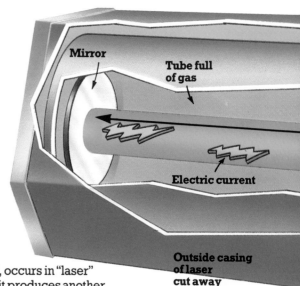

Mirror

Tube full of gas

Electric current

Outside casing of laser cut away to show inside

The electric current excites the atoms (or molecules) in the gas and they then give off or "emit" photons (light energy).

Some of the emitted photons hit other excited atoms. This causes them to give off identical photons. This is the Stimulated Emission of Radiation part of "laser".

Amplification, which means "making bigger", occurs in "laser" because when a photon hits an excited atom, it produces another photon identical to itself, both in energy and phase. Both photons can then hit other excited atoms and produce yet more photons, which in turn make further photons, and so on.

Making a laser beam

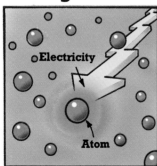

Electricity

Atom

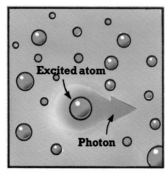

Excited atom

Photon

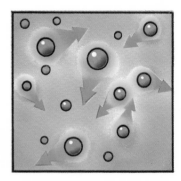

These pictures show what happens to the atoms and photons inside a laser. Electricity passes through the gas and some of its atoms absorb energy from it and become "excited".

Atoms cannot stay in this excited state and so return to normal by giving off their extra energy as a photon. This is called "spontaneous emission" and is not "lasing" – yet.

Lasing only occurs when over half the atoms are excited. This is known as an "inverted population" as it is opposite to the normal state, when few atoms are excited.

The gas tube has a mirror at each end. Some of the emitted photons hit the mirrors and are reflected back into the gas, for further amplification and stimulated emission. Only photons travelling parallel to the tube hit the mirrors. Photons travelling in other directions just go out of the tube.

The mirror at this end is only partially reflective and will let through some of the light. As long as the mirror reflects back enough photons to keep up the amplification, a beam of coherent, one colour, one direction laser light will be produced.

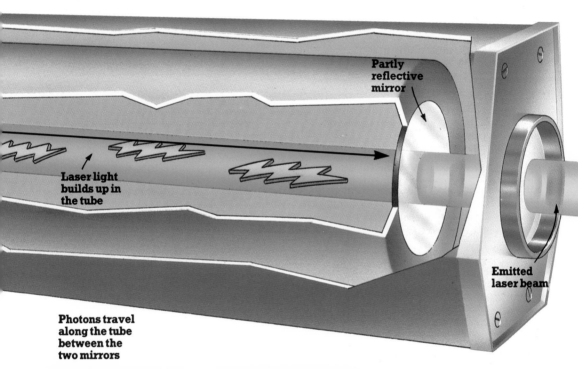

Partly reflective mirror

Laser light builds up in the tube

Emitted laser beam

Photons travel along the tube between the two mirrors

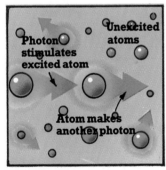

Photon stimulates excited atom

Unexcited atoms

Atom makes another photon

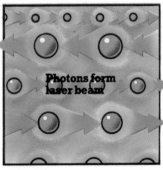

Photons form laser beam

Exciting lighting

Lasers are not the only lights to work by excitation. All light

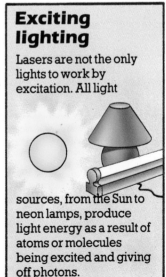

Photons hitting excited atoms produce another photon, but photons hitting unexcited atoms are lost. This is why an inverted population is necessary for lasing to occur.

The stimulated emission and amplification mean that lasing has begun. The laser light is reflected along the tube between the mirrors, producing a parallel beam, part of which is emitted.

sources, from the Sun to neon lamps, produce light energy as a result of atoms or molecules being excited and giving off photons.

Types of laser

The gas laser shown on the previous pages is just one type of laser. Lasers can be made from many different solids and liquids as well as from gases. The method of exciting substances to lase varies too; it can be electricity, light, chemical reaction or even another laser. This means that lasers can be matched to particular tasks. The low power laser that scans your shopping, for example, would not be at all useful for welding cars together or etching circuits on a microchip. The next four pages look at the different kinds of laser.

Gas lasers

Gas lasers are usually excited into lasing by an electric current. This picture shows a carbon dioxide (CO_2) laser with its casing off. CO_2 lasers are very common, but the sort that you are most likely to see is the helium neon (HeNe) laser. These produce a low power, red beam and are often used in schools as they are safe, small and relatively cheap. The argon (Ar) gas laser is widely used in medicine and some other gas lasers are krypton (Kr), and gold (Au) and copper (Cu) vapour where the metal has been vaporized into a kind of gas.

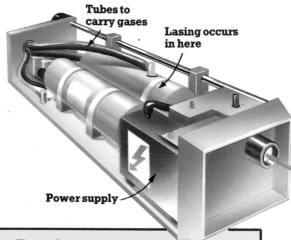

Tubes to carry gases

Lasing occurs in here

Power supply

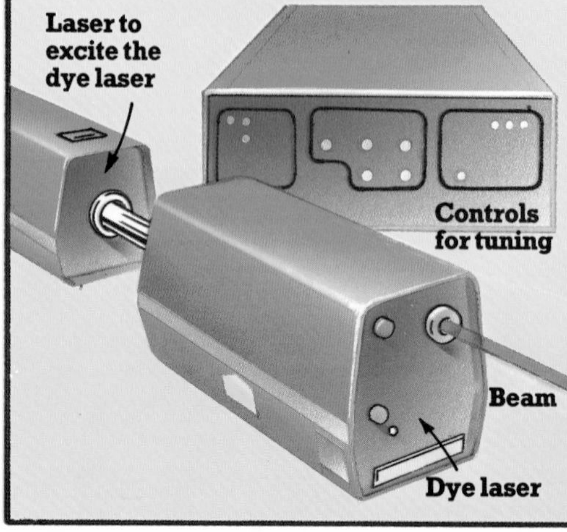

Dye lasers

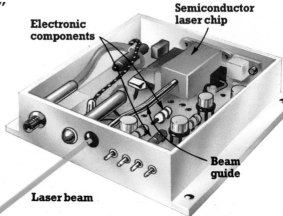

Laser to excite the dye laser

Controls for tuning

Beam

Dye laser

These are made from liquid which has been coloured by a simple dye. They produce a laser beam when excited by a very intense flash of ordinary light or another laser, as pictured here. The advantage of a dye laser is that they produce beams of different wavelengths. This happens because in a liquid the excited atoms provide a broad range of light. The laser has a prism to split this light into narrow wavelengths and so the beam can be "tuned" to different wavelengths.

Semiconductor laser "chips"

These are miniature lasers made from tiny pieces of solid material called semiconductors. (Semiconductors are used to make transistors and microchips.) Laser chips produce a tiny beam when excited by electricity. They are vital to modern telecommunications and are beginning to be used in lots of electronic equipment. This picture shows a laser chip inside a telecommunications receiver.

Semiconductor laser chip

Electronic components

Beam guide

Laser beam

Solid state lasers

Rod of synthetic ruby crystal

Flash tube makes brilliant light

"Solid state" lasers are made from rods of solid, transparent material, such as synthetic ruby and emerald. They are excited into lasing by a brilliant flash of light, pictured above. These lasers have to be made from clear crystals that will let in the light. The very first laser was a solid state ruby laser. Other solid state lasers are neodymium-yag (Nd-YAG) and neodymium in glass (Nd-glass) and they are used in industry for cutting, drilling and engraving.

Chemical lasers

When some chemicals are mixed together they react violently, producing a great deal of heat. This can excite the atoms of the chemicals into lasing. Hydrogen and fluorine react like this, producing hydrogen fluoride (HF) gas in an excited state; and a laser beam. Carbon monoxide (CO), hydrogen bromide (HBr) and hydrogen cyanide (HCN) lasers all work in this way too.

Laser beam

Laser names

Lasers are usually given the name of the substances from which they are made; carbon dioxide, argon, ruby and so on. This name is often shortened to the letters which are the symbol for the chemical, like HeNe for helium neon. The type of laser is often also mentioned, as in gold vapour laser.

Laser colours

Lasers produce beams of different colours depending upon the substance they are made from. Ruby laser beams are red, like the crystals. Every chemical produces a particular wavelength and colour. For example, sodium street lamps shine orange, neon signs are red and argon lights are greeny-blue. You can test this by carefully burning various chemicals in a flame. Salt contains sodium and will make it flare orange, potassium flares purple and copper will make it green.

Laser beams

These two pages look at the beams of different kinds of laser and how they vary. The wavelength and colour, intensity, power and length of beams all depend upon the type of laser. A laser's uses depend upon what its beam can do.

Pulsed lasers

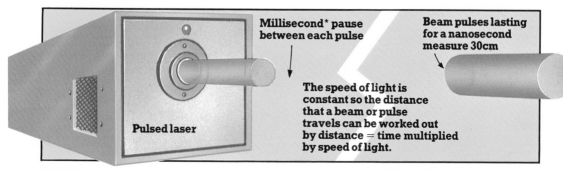

Millisecond* pause between each pulse

Beam pulses lasting for a nanosecond measure 30cm

The speed of light is constant so the distance that a beam or pulse travels can be worked out by distance = time multiplied by speed of light.

Pulsed laser

Pulsed lasers produce a beam as a series of extremely short pulses of light, rather than as a single steady beam. Lasers which are not pulsed are called continuous wave (CW) lasers. Some kinds, such as the CO_2 laser, can be either continuous or pulsed. Pulsed lasers work by emitting light only when the lasing material is at peak excitement. Some lasers produce hundreds or thousands of pulses every second and these look continuous. Others produce only one pulse every ten minutes or longer. The pulse length can vary from a few thousandths to less than a billionth of a second. The power of the light energy in a pulse is variable too.

Laser power

A laser's power is measured in watts, like light bulbs. A 10 watt bulb would hardly give enough light to read this book, but a 10 watt laser beam could be powerful enough to burn a hole right through the book. This is because laser light is concentrated in an intense beam, rather than spread out in all directions. Lasers vary in power from a few watts to many millions and are measured like this: kilowatt = thousand watts
megawatt = million watts
gigawatt = thousand million watts
terrawatt = million million watts

Pulsed lasers are the most powerful as their light energy is concentrated in rapid pulses. A low wattage continuous wave laser may be able to produce the same amount of energy as a large pulsed laser, but it will take much longer to do it.

High power, pulsed and CW lasers are used for things like drilling and cutting metals while low power CW lasers are used for playing laser discs. Medium power lasers are used for things like surgery.

106

Tiny measurements of time have these special names: millisecond = a thousandth of a sec,

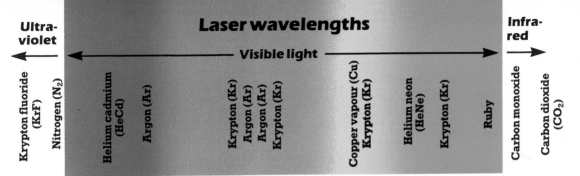

Laser wavelengths

Ultra-violet ←

Infra-red →

← Visible light →

Krypton fluoride (KrF)

Nitrogen (N₂)

Helium cadmium (HeCd)

Argon (Ar)

Krypton (Kr)
Argon (Ar)
Argon (Ar)
Krypton (Kr)

Copper vapour (Cu)
Krypton (Kr)

Helium neon (HeNe)

Krypton (Kr)

Ruby

Carbon monoxide

Carbon dioxide (CO₂)

This chart shows which lasers produce which wavelengths. Some produce beams of more than one wavelength and dye lasers can be tuned from ultra-violet to infra-red. Each wavelength is a particular, constant measurement. Visible light is between 400 and 750 nanometres (thousand-millionths of a metre) and covers the spectrum from violet to dark red. The infra-red and ultra-violet bands are much bigger than the visible band and so do not fit onto this page.

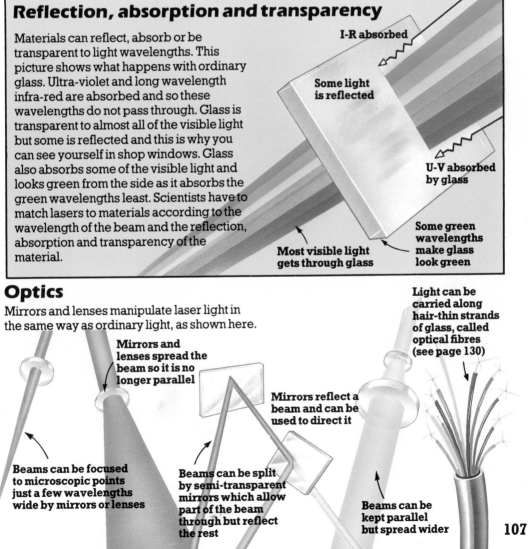

Reflection, absorption and transparency

Materials can reflect, absorb or be transparent to light wavelengths. This picture shows what happens with ordinary glass. Ultra-violet and long wavelength infra-red are absorbed and so these wavelengths do not pass through. Glass is transparent to almost all of the visible light but some is reflected and this is why you can see yourself in shop windows. Glass also absorbs some of the visible light and looks green from the side as it absorbs the green wavelengths least. Scientists have to match lasers to materials according to the wavelength of the beam and the reflection, absorption and transparency of the material.

I-R absorbed

Some light is reflected

U-V absorbed by glass

Some green wavelengths make glass look green

Most visible light gets through glass

Optics

Mirrors and lenses manipulate laser light in the same way as ordinary light, as shown here.

Mirrors and lenses spread the beam so it is no longer parallel

Mirrors reflect a beam and can be used to direct it

Light can be carried along hair-thin strands of glass, called optical fibres (see page 130)

Beams can be focused to microscopic points just a few wavelengths wide by mirrors or lenses

Beams can be split by semi-transparent mirrors which allow part of the beam through but reflect the rest

Beams can be kept parallel but spread wider

107

microsecond = a millionth, nanosecond = a thousand millionth, picosecond = a million millionth.

Lasers in industry

Lasers are used in industry to cut, drill, weld and engrave lots of things from the hardest steel and even harder diamonds to fabrics, paper and plastics. Many industrial lasers are vast, powerful machines, usually working automatically and often under computer control. The next six pages explain how lasers do these things and why they are beginning to be used instead of conventional tools like drills and saws. Perhaps lasers will one day be common DIY tools at home too.

Working with lasers

This picture shows a helium-cadmium laser being tried out on a test bench. This small gas laser is used for laser printing (see page 129) and is about the size of a slide projector. Some industrial lasers are huge and fill a whole room.

The beam

Light comes out of the laser as a parallel beam, which is usually unable to burn a hole. It has to be focused to concentrate its power to do this.

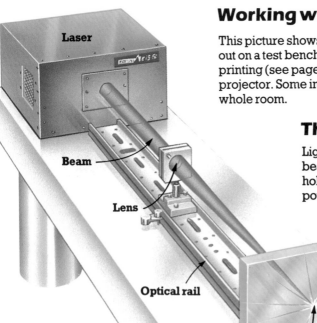

Laser

Beam

Lens

Optical rail

Lens slides along optical rail to be focused

Beam focused to tiny point to drill a hole

Focusing

The beam is focused to a point with one or more lenses between the laser and the material on which it is working. The spot size and intensity of the beam is varied by adjusting the position and type of lenses. The power of the spot depends upon the kind of laser being used.

Stability

In some applications it is important to keep the laser and optical equipment quite still, as vibrations affect the laser's accuracy. This test bench has special legs which absorb vibrations to stop them reaching the table top.

Control

Industrial lasers are often electronically controlled to produce beams of the right kind, a the right time. This is especially important with pulsed lasers. The focusing lenses and mirrors are also controlled. This makes lasers especially suitable tools for jobs which can be done automatically.

Drilling with light

Focused sunlight

Paper

Move lens up and down

Take great care – the spot will be very hot and can burn you or cause a fire

You can test for yourself the principle of focusing light to make a hole. Use a magnifying glass to focus sunlight onto a piece of paper. Move the lens up and down to get a tiny, concentrated spot.

Choosing lasers

Lasers have to be carefully matched in power and wavelength to the job and materials they have to work on. This picture shows a laser being used to strip paint from an aircraft which needs repainting. The laser is at a wavelength that only the paint layers absorb, and so the beam burns them off. The metal beneath simply reflects the beam and is left unharmed. A laser can do this job more quickly and cheaply than other methods, such as chemical stripping.

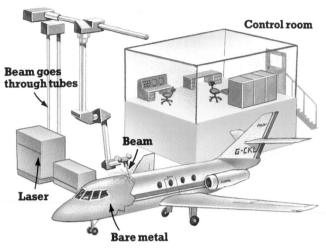

Control room

Beam goes through tubes

Beam

Laser

Bare metal

Directing the beam

A great advantage of the laser is that the beams can so easily be directed to where they are wanted. The laser itself is stationary but the beam can travel either along optical fibres, or simply be reflected by mirrors along a path. Light can be directed to and used in small or awkward places which would be inaccessible to ordinary tools.

The picture below shows a high power hand operated laser welding machine. The beam is directed by mirrors, inside a flexible tube. The operator can vary the power as well as freely move the beam.

Outer casing cut away to show inside

Mirror

Oxygen pipe

Lens focuses beam to a hot point

Oxygen makes beam burn hotter

Nozzle

The picture above shows the inside of a laser drilling tool that uses mirrors to guide the beam. The beam is simply reflected by the mirrors to the lens which focuses it, and then goes out through a nozzle. A jet of oxygen is used as it makes the beam hotter and more efficient for some drilling uses.

Helmet and visor

Hinged joint and mirror make beam guide flexible

Controls

Protective clothes prevent sparks burning the operator

Beam guide

Drilling and cutting

The most common industrial uses for lasers are cutting and drilling. An advantage of a laser beam is that as it is simply powerful light, it cannot wear out or clog up, as saws and drill bits do. Lasers are very fast and clean and also more accurate and precise than conventional tools.

How lasers make holes

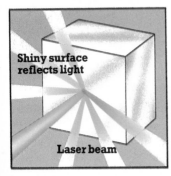

Shiny surface reflects light

Laser beam

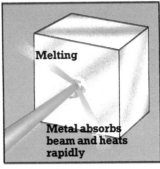

Melting

Metal absorbs beam and heats rapidly

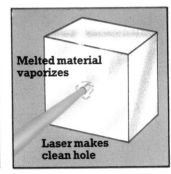

Melted material vaporizes

Laser makes clean hole

The focused beam heats the surface of the material. Shiny things like metals reflect much of the beam at first, so heat slowest.

The surface starts to melt. Metals begin to heat rapidly now as the surface is dulled by melting and there is less reflection.

Almost immediately, the melted material gets so hot it boils away – vaporizes. The beam goes in deeper, making a clean hole.

Drilling

A laser drills by vaporizing the material in a hole as fast as possible. This is best done by pulsed lasers as they deliver short, high energy beams. The material in a hole is completely removed by the vaporization. With an ordinary mechanical drill bit, tiny pieces of waste material are forced out of the hole. This "swarf" clogs up machinery and cuts workers' hands. A laser leaves a clean hole with no swarf.

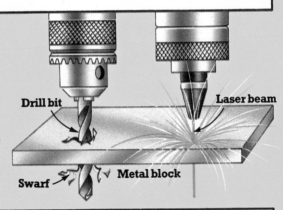

Drill bit

Laser beam

Swarf

Metal block

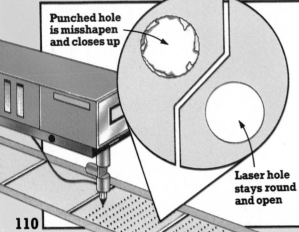

Punched hole is misshapen and closes up

Laser hole stays round and open

Laser holes

The picture on the left shows a laser drilling tiny holes in stretchy plastic bandages and compares a laser hole with a punched hole. Lasers are especially good at cutting and drilling this sort of material and fibrous things like paper and cloth, as they are "non contact" tools. This means that the beam does not actually touch the surface it is working, so does not push it out of shape. Punched holes and cuts tend to close up, as the materials are squashed or stretched in the process.

Cutting

Lasers use the same principle for cutting as for drilling, but either the laser, or the material, moves so the beam traces a path and makes a cut. This cut is called the "kerf" and it is very clean and narrow as the laser cuts by vaporization. The area on either side of the kerf is often slightly damaged by the beam. This is known as the "HAZ", short for Heat Affected Zone. The laser is controlled to keep the HAZ as small as possible. The kerf and HAZ cut in foam rubber are illustrated in the circle below.

Robot arm

Beam guide

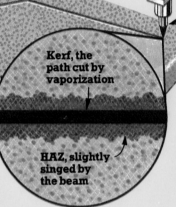

Kerf, the path cut by vaporization

HAZ, slightly singed by the beam

The picture above shows an industrial robot which is cutting complex shapes out of foam rubber, using a laser. The laser is behind the robot as it is too big to fix onto it. The beam travels along the guide tube, reflected by mirrors inside. Both the laser and robot are computer controlled, working to a program that tells the robot what shape to trace and turns the laser on and off.

Shape cutter

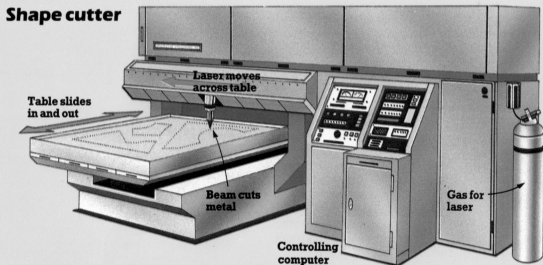

Laser moves across table

Table slides in and out

Beam cuts metal

Gas for laser

Controlling computer

This machine uses a laser to cut out shapes in metal sheeting. The metal is fixed to a motor driven table which slides in and out under the laser. The beam is directed by mirrors through a nozzle and is driven in the opposite direction across the table. The shapes to be cut out are programmed into the computer which controls the movements of both the laser and table.

Engraving and welding

The precision, accuracy and easy control of laser beams make them excellent tools for engraving, welding and treating the surfaces of various materials, as well as for cutting and drilling. These two pages show how lasers are used for these tasks.

Computer controlled engraving

This mirror moves beam left to right

Lenses focus laser beam

This mirror moves beam up and down

Laser beam

Engraving is similar to cutting, except the beam does not go all the way through. This picture shows how a computer-controlled laser engraver works. The beam is engraving letters and numbers onto an electronic component.

The characters to be engraved are typed on a computer keyboard, together with instructions about size, shape and style of printing. Instructions about the speed, depth and power of beam are also given.

The beam is focused by lenses and made to follow a path by moving mirrors. These direct and focus the laser beam on the surface of the component, making it engrave the correct characters. The beam itself moves to trace the path. This sort of set up can also be used to engrave pictures and all kinds of shapes as well as letters and numbers.

Controlling computer

Electronic component

N-3 MN110 .24

Welding

This picture shows a laser beam welding two sheets of steel together. The beam melts – but does not vaporize – a cone-shaped area of metal as it moves across the join between the two sheets. The molten metal from the two sheets mixes together and quickly solidifies when the beam moves away, to form a strong weld.

Laser welding is very fast. Big, powerful CO_2 lasers can weld steel of 2.5cm thickness at a rate of two metres a second. It is also very accurate and clean as the HAZ is small.

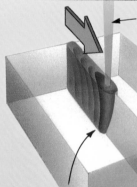

Laser beam

Molten metals mix and solidify as laser moves on

Cone-shaped molten area goes down through steel

Metal away from beam is unaffected by beam, so does not scorch or melt

Spot welding

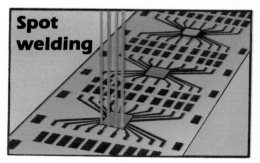

This laser beam has been split into four and is welding microchips into their cases. Lasers are good for this, being precise and accurate even at such tiny sizes. Another advantage is that the beam cannot contaminate the chip as it does not touch it.

Pulse welding

Each ridge is formed by a beam pulse

This metal case contains explosives. The end is sealed onto the sides by a pulsed laser which makes a ridged seam. The heat and depth of the beam are so precisely controlled that the explosive, only a millimetre below the weld, is unaffected.

Vacuum welding

Beam passes right through glass, like any light

As it is a form of light, a laser beam can do things that are impossible with conventional tools. This beam is welding the filament inside a car headlamp. The beam goes through the glass and is unaffected by the vacuum or special gas inside.

Surface treatments

Lots of materials can be improved if they are heated and very often this treatment is needed only on the surface. Steel, for example, can be made harder for longer life by rapid heating followed by rapid cooling. This process changes the actual composition of a very thin layer of the metal at the surface. The picture below shows a knife edge being hardened in this way, by laser. The same treatment is also used on engine parts for cars and planes to stop them wearing out quickly.

Rapid heating where beam hits steel

Rapid cooling as beam moves on

Another treatment is heating, followed by slow cooling – this is known as "annealing". It is a process used on the special crystals of semiconductors used to make microchips. These crystals have to be pure and free from imperfections. Unfortunately they often have natural strains and cracks in the material that forms the crystal. By heating the surface and allowing it to cool slowly, these crystal defects can be broken and allowed to re-form.

This picture shows the changes that annealing can cause in the crystal structure and how it smooths out the surface of the semiconductor.

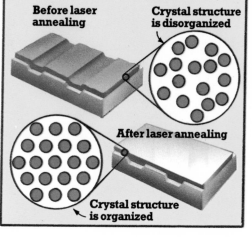

Before laser annealing

Crystal structure is disorganized

After laser annealing

Crystal structure is organized

Laser discs

One of the places that you may come across lasers in the future is when playing music and video discs. A new kind of disc, which is recorded and played by laser beam, has been developed. They have silvery, mirror-like surfaces which reflect light in a rainbow spectrum, like the one pictured here. Video discs are about the size of an LP and hold both pictures and sound. Audio discs are sound only, much smaller and often known as compact or digital discs. These two pages look at how laser discs work and what is special about them.

How laser discs work

This picture shows a laser disc being scanned by a semiconductor laser chip. Some players use small HeNe lasers instead. It also shows the optical equipment of lenses, mirrors and so on which are inside the player.

The laser disc has a very reflective metallic surface, covered by a protective coating of clear plastic. There are microscopically tiny indentations in this surface, called "pits" and the plain areas in between are "flats". The circle on the right shows the pits and flats greatly magnified.

The player spins the disc and scans it with the laser beam, which moves straight across the disc from the centre to the edge. The shiny surface reflects the beam back into the player, where it is picked up by an electronic device. This produces an electrical signal when it detects light.

The pits and flats on the disc reflect the laser beam differently, producing a varying beam. This in turn makes the detector produce a varying electrical signal, which the player de-codes back into video pictures and sounds.

Laser disc

Magnified view

Pit

Flat

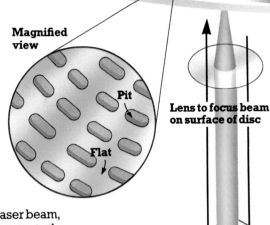

Lens to focus beam on surface of disc

Mirror bends beam

Beam to disc

Beam reflected by disc

Detector

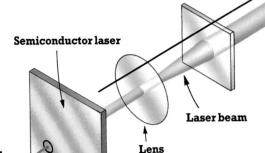

Semiconductor laser

This lens bends only the beam reflected by the disc

Lens

Laser beam

Reflected beam has been varied by pits and flats

Lens

Recording laser discs

The pits and flats are originally made by a laser beam, controlled by the electrical signals recorded with video cameras and microphones. Only one disc is recorded in this way and it acts as a "master" to make moulds from which all the copies are pressed. You can't use laser discs for recording at home.

Video discs

Video disc player

This picture shows a video disc player and discs, with an ordinary TV to show the pictures. Each side of the disc holds up to an hour of video, or 54,000 still pictures.

Why laser discs are special

The way that laser discs are played and recorded makes them different from other kinds of records. Their plastic coating makes them amazingly tough and they can be thrown about – even stamped on – without much ill effect and will play even if scratched and dirty. This is because the laser beam is precisely focused only on the reflective surface, as pictured below. Any imperfections on the clear, outer layer are out of focus and ignored.

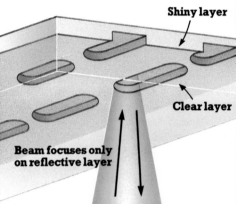

Shiny layer

Clear layer

Beam focuses only on reflective layer

Another advantage of laser discs is that they never wear out. There is no physical contact between the disc and player – only a beam of light, too weak to harm either. Even the players are more reliable as there are fewer mechanical parts to break down.

Digital discs

Audio discs are also known as compact discs because of their small size and as digital discs because they are recorded using computer processing. Digital recordings are better quality than the ordinary kind as they can deal with a wider range of sounds. Many problems such as background hissing and crackling are actually created by conventional recording techniques and so avoided on digital discs. Video discs are not digital.

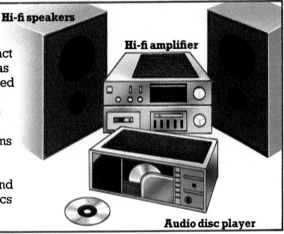

Hi-fi speakers

Hi-fi amplifier

Audio disc player

115

Medical lasers

Lasers can drill, cut and weld not only metals and plastics, but also people. They are being used in many kinds of medical operations and proving to be very efficient. Lasers are replacing the surgeon's scalpel and this is often called "bloodless surgery" as the heat of the beam seals up blood vessels around the cut and prevents bleeding. Beams are also used in operations to destroy growths. There is little or no pain and healing is faster than in conventional surgery.

These two pages show some of the laser's many medical uses.

Inside the stomach

This picture shows a laser beam operating on an ulcer inside a patient's stomach. The beam travels through an optical fibre which is part of an instrument called an endoscope.

The endoscope

Endoscopes are made from bundles of optical fibres and thin tubes, put together into a cable about as thick as a finger. They are slim enough to pass down the patient's throat, without causing too much discomfort. The extra tubes provide air, water and suction to clean the area on which the beam is working.

The laser

This operation is being done by an argon laser which produces a green beam. Nd-YAG lasers are also used for surgery but as they produce an invisible, infra-red beam, they have to be mixed with a red helium neon laser beam, so that the surgeon can see where it is.

Ulcers

Ulcers are arteries that bleed into the stomach. The laser treats them by heating the end of the artery and welding the opening shut. The weld is made by a tiny scar which forms over the burn. The tissue surrounding the ulcer is not affected by the laser, as the beam is precisely focused on the artery.

Lasers can also be used to remove unwanted growths such as tumours, stones and cysts which form on internal organs.

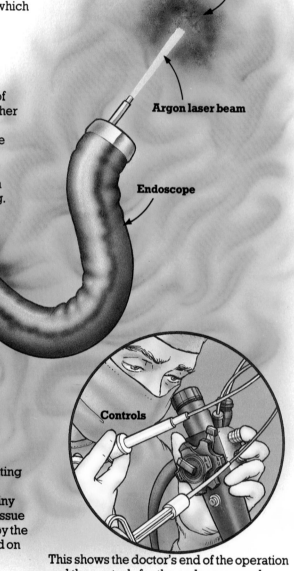

Ulcer

Argon laser beam

Endoscope

Controls

This shows the doctor's end of the operation and the controls for the endoscope and laser. The doctor can see inside the stomach via optical fibres in the endoscope.

Skin treatment

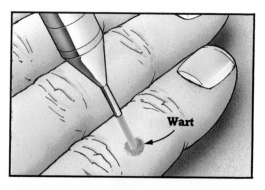

Wart

The precision of a laser is also used on the outside of the body. They remove warts, and other growths, leaving the skin around untouched. Lasers are so accurate they can peel skin away in very thin layers.

Tooth decay

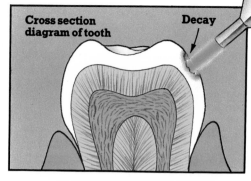

Cross section diagram of tooth

Decay

Dentists are beginning to test lasers for drilling decay from teeth. Only the dark, rotten areas absorb the laser beam. The white, healthy parts of the tooth reflect it and are left unaffected, as shown above.

Eye surgery

The laser's most common medical use is in eye surgery. Some eye defects occur when the retina is detached from the back of the eye. A laser can weld the retina back into place without the need to cut open the eye. The beam passes straight through the eye ball without affecting it, just as ordinary light does. The beam is focused on the retina by the lens of the eye itself. A small heat scar results and makes the weld.

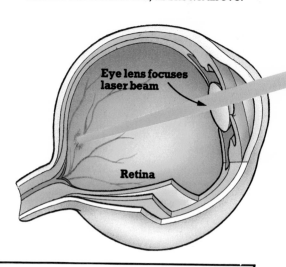

Eye lens focuses laser beam

Retina

Removing marks

Lasers can remove markings such as tattoos and some birth marks. The large red birth marks known as "port wine stains" are the most easily treated. A green wavelength argon laser is used as the red coloured areas of the birth mark will absorb more of the beam than the normal coloured skin. This picture shows a red beam being used on a green tattoo. The laser burns away tiny areas of the marking so that new, uncoloured skin will grow to replace it. The treatment is almost painless but takes a long time as only small areas can be treated in one session.

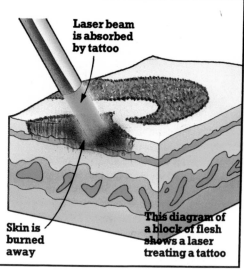

Laser beam is absorbed by tattoo

Skin is burned away

This diagram of a block of flesh shows a laser treating a tattoo

Holograms

A hologram is a kind of photograph, made with a laser and recorded on a flat plate of photographic film or glass. The unique thing about holograms is that they have a three-dimensional (3D) image which looks solid. The image seems to hang in space; either in front of the plate or behind it or even right across it. As you move in relation to the hologram you get a different view of the image, just as you do when looking at a real object. Holograms are so convincing, you feel as if you could grab the image or put your hand right into the picture. The next six pages look at what holograms are, how they are made and their uses.

Designed by Dicken Eames
Produced by Light Fantastic (UK) Ltd.

This is a photograph of a hologram. It is very difficult to show the 3D nature of holograms in a book, which is 2D.

The third dimension

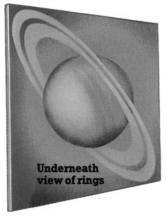

Underneath view of rings

Side-on view of rings

Top view of rings

These pictures illustrate three views of a hologram of a model of Saturn. The view of the planet and its rings changes as you move in relation to the hologram. You can see the rings from underneath, side-on and above. The whole image changes as you move, unlike a photograph which looks the same no matter where you are. This realistic changing image is called "parallax".

How holograms work

You only see things because light is reflected from them and detected by your eyes. A hologram looks so realistic because it is an exact recording of the light waves reflected from an object. When the image is reconstructed it reflects light in just the same way as the object originally did. This gives the hologram its convincing illusion of reality. Light reaching your eyes from the hologram is the same as that from the real object.

Real object   **Hologram**

All-round view

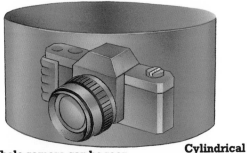

Whole camera can be seen from different angles

Cylindrical plate

A flat plate has only limited parallax, rather as a window does. By recording holograms from all angles on a cylindrical plate, it is possible to make a 360° holographic image. The image seems to float in the cylinder.

Whole image

The word hologram means "whole picture". If a plate is broken, each piece has the whole image on it, not just the part it showed originally. The view, though, is more restricted.

Looking at holograms

Reflection hologram

Transmission hologram

Unreconstructed hologram

A hologram looks like a fuzzy blur until lit by a light. This is called "reconstruction" and makes the image visible. Some can only be seen when lit by a laser but most need only a spotlight, although it may have to be at a particular angle. There are two kinds of hologram and they differ in the way they are reconstructed. Reflection holograms are lit by light shining on the front of the plate. Transmission holograms by light shining through the plate. In both cases it is the light from the plate that makes you see the image.

Holographic colour

Holograms do not give true colour reproduction. Their colour depends upon the colour of the laser used to make the hologram. Multi-coloured images are created by using different lasers to light different parts of the objects being pictured.

A different kind of multi-coloured hologram, called a rainbow hologram, changes colour as you move in relation to it. It covers the whole spectrum from red to violet.

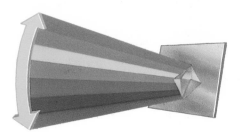

This picture shows how a rainbow hologram changes colour. Holographic colours are very brilliant and vivid because they are made from pure, one wavelength light.

119

and focus a laser beam. The image of an object is recorded on a plate, which is covered by an emulsion of light sensitive chemicals. The plate is exposed both from direct laser light and laser light reflected by making a permanent record of the object. Ordinary film records a photograph by chemical changes too. The picture below shows how the equipment is set up to make a hologram of a telephone.

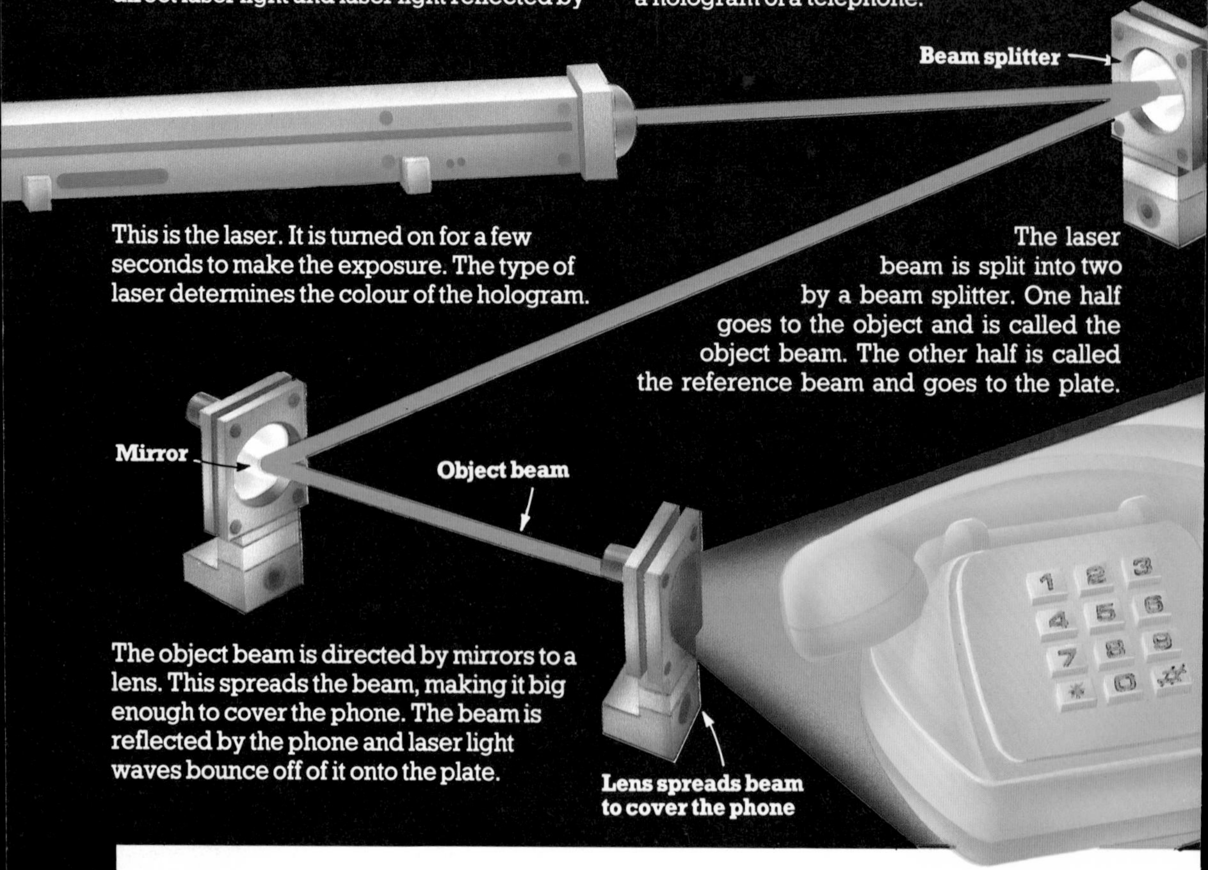

Beam splitter ⟶

This is the laser. It is turned on for a few seconds to make the exposure. The type of laser determines the colour of the hologram.

The laser beam is split into two by a beam splitter. One half goes to the object and is called the object beam. The other half is called the reference beam and goes to the plate.

Mirror

Object beam

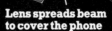

The object beam is directed by mirrors to a lens. This spreads the beam, making it big enough to cover the phone. The beam is reflected by the phone and laser light waves bounce off of it onto the plate.

Lens spreads beam to cover the phone

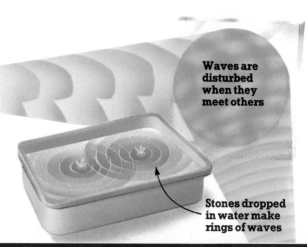

Interference patterns

The interference pattern made on the plate by the laser beams is a record of the object. The lightwaves in the reflected object beam are out of phase with those of the undisturbed reference beam. The differences between them are "measurements" of the object, in lightwaves.

You can make a kind of interference pattern by dropping two stones into water. The two sets of ripples disturb each other and make an interference pattern where they meet.

Waves are disturbed when they meet others

Stones dropped in water make rings of waves

Holography table

It is vital to keep everything as still as possible – any vibrations, even sound waves, will blur the finished hologram. The set-up is usually put on a special table made out of sand and inflated tyre tubes, resting on a concrete floor, to absorb unwanted vibrations.

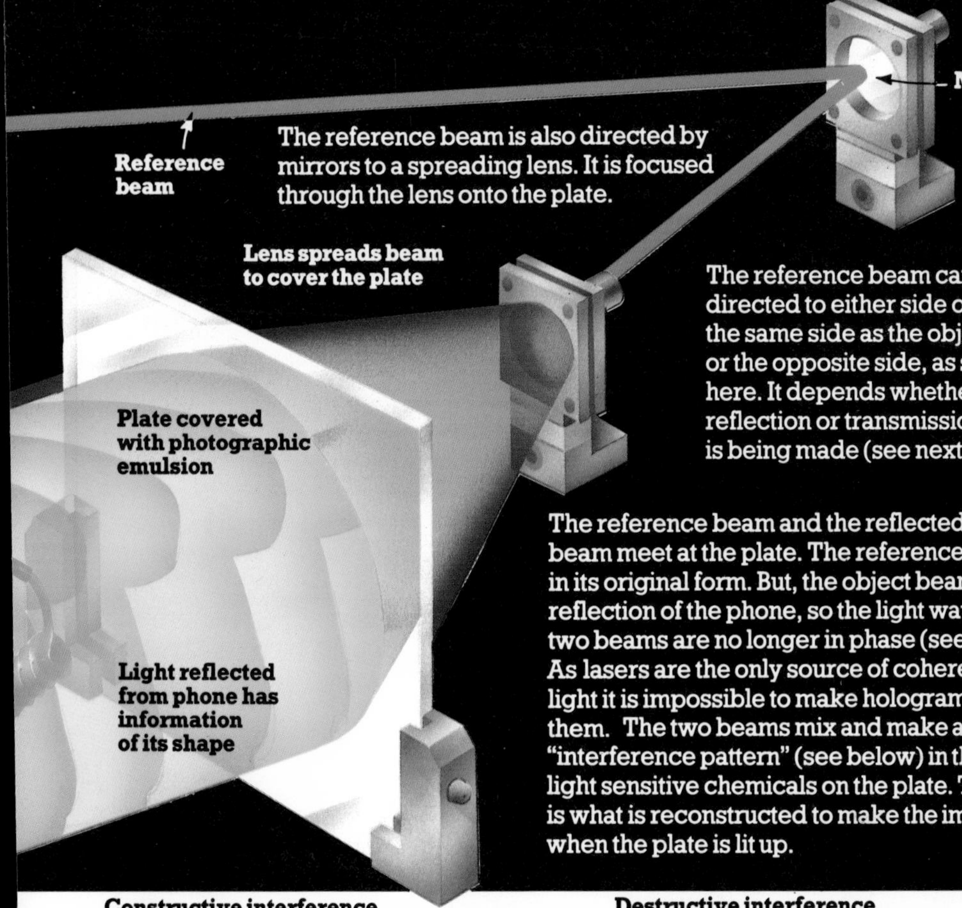

Mirror

Reference beam

The reference beam is also directed by mirrors to a spreading lens. It is focused through the lens onto the plate.

Lens spreads beam to cover the plate

Plate covered with photographic emulsion

Light reflected from phone has information of its shape

The reference beam can be directed to either side of the plate – the same side as the object beam, or the opposite side, as shown here. It depends whether a reflection or transmission hologram is being made (see next page).

The reference beam and the reflected object beam meet at the plate. The reference beam is still in its original form. But, the object beam is a reflection of the phone, so the light waves of the two beams are no longer in phase (see page 101). As lasers are the only source of coherent (in phase) light it is impossible to make holograms without them. The two beams mix and make an "interference pattern" (see below) in the light sensitive chemicals on the plate. This is what is reconstructed to make the image when the plate is lit up.

Constructive interference

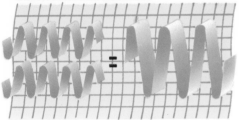

Destructive interference

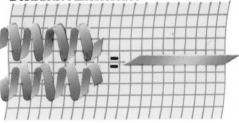

The two pictures above show what happens when two sets of lightwaves meet. If the peaks of one coincide with the peaks of the other, they add together to make a wave double the original size. This is called "constructive interference". If peaks coincide with

troughs they cancel each other out. This is called "destructive interference". In-between stages make waves of varying sizes. It is these combined waves that make the fuzzy ripples of the interference pattern, visible on the plate.

Making holograms ... 2

After being exposed, the holographic plate has to be processed in a similar way to photographic film. The image must then be reconstructed by a beam shining from the same direction as the reference beam that made the hologram. The two pictures below show the differences in the making of transmission and reflection holograms.

Reflection hologram

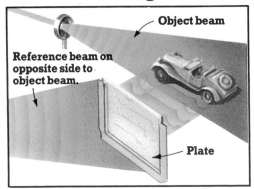

If the reference beam is shone onto the opposite side of the plate to the object the hologram will be a reflection hologram, visible by light reflecting off it.

Transmission hologram

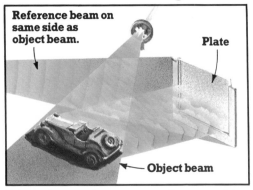

If the reference beam was on the same side as the object then the plate will have to be lit from that side and will be a transmission hologram.

Holographic movies

At the moment holography is not practical for making proper moving pictures. It is possible to make a simple hologram "movie" by using a sequence of holograms side by side along a plate. You see the image "move" as you walk past. This sort of hologram is usually made by shining lasers through recorded cine film, as it is necessary to have hundreds of images to show even a tiny movement, like a kick or wave of the hand.

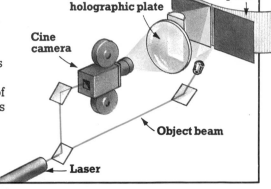

Multiple images

Several images can be recorded on top of each other on a single plate by changing the angle of the reference beam used for each. The different pictures will become visible when the angle of the viewing beam is changed – as happens when the viewer moves in relation to the plate. This is one way of making a simple animated hologram, which works rather like a flick picture.

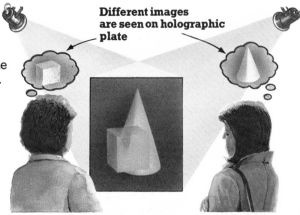

122

Three ways of 3D

Real image hologram

Image plane hologram

Virtual image hologram

A holographic plate is a flat sheet but the image can appear in different places in relation to it. A hologram can seem to sink backwards – this is known as a "virtual image". More dramatically, the image can project into space in front of the plate, springing out at you – this is called a "real image". The image may also straddle across the plate, half of it sinking back, half of it coming forwards – known as an "image plane". The pictures above show these three kinds of hologram.

Making a real image hologram

The holographic set up shown on the previous pages will produce virtual image holograms. Real image and image plane holograms are not made directly from a real object, but from a virtual image hologram.

To do this, the image is reconstructed but lit from the wrong side; so a transmission hologram is lit from in front, a reflection hologram from behind. The image appears hanging in front of the plate – as a real image – but it is inside out and back to front. This is known as a "pseudoscopic"* image. These pictures show how a hologram of the letter F changes when pseudoscopic. The hologram made from the pseudoscopic image will also be a virtual image, but when it is lit from the wrong side, it will be a real image hologram and the right way round. This is because when something that is already inside out is turned inside out, it becomes right way round again. **123**

Pronounced syou-do-scopick

Using holograms

Holography is now at about the stage that photography reached around 1900. Perhaps in the next century you will be taking holographic snaps, reading holographic magazines and watching 3D laser TV. You can already see holograms in galleries, museums, exhibitions, buy them to hang on your wall or made into jewellery and even find them printed in books and magazines. One limitation to holography is the fact that holograms are always exactly the same size as the original object. So, holograms of things bigger than the largest plates, about a metre square, cannot be made and reductions are not possible either. These pages show some uses for holograms.

Holograms can make very impressive advertising displays. This real image of a hand and diamond bracelet was used by a jeweller's shop in New York. The image seemed to hang a metre out from the window.

Holograms can be printed, by a special process, onto silvery plastic. They are used for books, LP covers, and even sweet wrappers. Printed holograms are not so clear or detailed as those on plates.

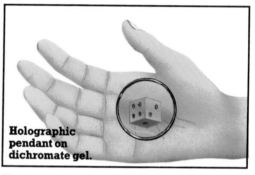

Holographic pendant on dichromate gel.

Holograms can be recorded on a light-sensitive jelly called dichromate gel. The hologram is covered by glass to make jewellery, or used on other clear containers such as jars.

Telephone call by hologram

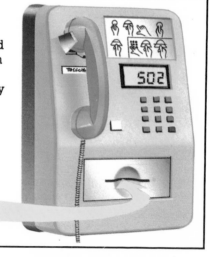

This credit card can be used with new, computerized pay phones. The card has a strip of printed hologram on the back. The hologram is not a picture, but a special forgery proof pattern. The strip is scanned by an infra-red optical device in the phone. While a call is being made the scanner slowly destroys the strip as the credit is used up. The phone controls the scanner's speed, according to the cost of the call and shows how much credit is left on the card at the end.

Nuclear safety

This picture shows a hologram of the core of a nuclear reactor used to generate electricity. Scientists have to carry out safety checks, looking for cracks and other faults. They cannot do this by getting close to the core as it is dangerously radioactive. A hologram provides all the information that the real thing could and is so accurate that the image can even be examined under a microscope.

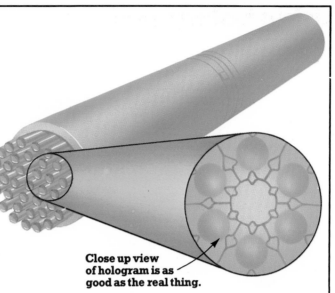

Close up view of hologram is as good as the real thing.

Stress check

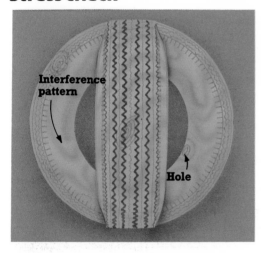

Interference pattern

Hole

This picture is a hologram of a motor car tyre. The swirling patterns show the stresses that build up in the tyre when it moves. They are recorded by making two holograms on one plate using a pulsed laser. One is made when the tyre is still, the other when it is moving. The two images do not exactly overlap and this creates an interference pattern in the hologram. The pattern indicates areas of stress and can show faults, such as holes or weak spots. Tyres are not the only things to be tested with this technique. All kinds of things, from beer cans to jet turbines, have to be measured for stress and can be checked in this way.

Credit card security

Embossed holograms are being used to make credit cards forgery proof. As holograms are difficult to make, forgers cannot copy a card which has a hologram of the company's symbol on it.

Keeping records

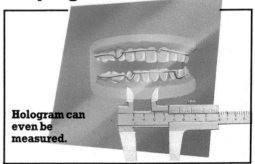

Hologram can even be measured.

Holograms provide as much information as a solid object, yet take up much less room, being thin, flat plates. They are being used as visual records for many things from dentures to art treasures.

125

Laser light shows

Although lasers are important to areas as diverse as engineering and medicine, they are not especially visible when being used in these ways. You are most likely actually to see lasers at pop concerts, on TV and in films, in discos, as street decorations and at shows devoted just to laser light. They are used in these ways because laser light is incredibly beautiful and can make wonderful effects. These pages picture and explain some of the laser light effects that you may see.

Solid light

Sheets and tunnels of light can be made by shining the beams onto clouds and mist bellowed out by smoke machines. The effect is created by particles in the clouds reflecting the light.

Rhythm pulsing

Lasers can be pulsed in time with the beat of pop music, as pictured above. This is done by an electronic device which uses the music's electrical signals to control the beams.

Fans

Huge fan shapes of light are made by lenses that spread and divide the beams. They can be moved up and down and rolled from side to side to make interwoven patterns of light.

Computer control

The lasers and optical equipment are controlled by computer from the console pictured here. The operator can work everything manually but most shows are so complex they are usually preprogrammed to create the effects.

The effects are done using mirrors and lenses to split, spread, move and direct the laser beams. There are huge projectors to house all this optical equipment and the lasers. The lasers used for light shows are safe when used properly, but could cause burns or damage eyes if shone directly at people.

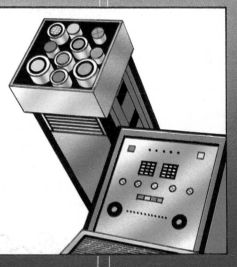

These pictures show the kind of patterns laser beams can make.

The beams are directed into these complex paths by special lenses, prisms and mirrors which rotate and vibrate to direct and "shape" the laser beam.

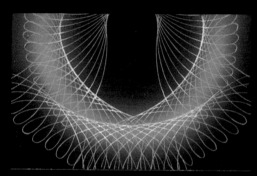

The laser beams do not actually make these shapes. They trace round the path so fast that the eye is fooled into seeing the shapes as if they are hanging in mid-air.

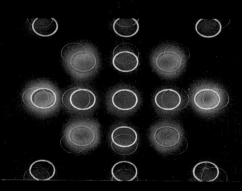

This technique can even be used to make light writing and draw pictures. Perhaps lasers will one day be used for signwriting

Krypton lasers which produce beams of four colours – red, gold, green and blue – are often used in light shows. The colours can be separated and mixed by directing the beam through a prism which splits the light into different wavelengths. Dye lasers are also popular as they can be "tuned" to produce lots of wavelengths and so almost any colour.

Silhouettes

Light cannot pass through solid objects so putting something in the way of a beam can produce a dramatic result.

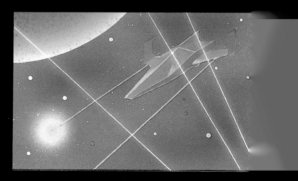

Lasers are often used in films to create the effects shown on these pages. But the death rays from "laser" guns and swords of sci-fi adventures are usually painted on the film,

Laser communications

An important and fast growing use for lasers is the storing, processing and communication of information. Lasers now transmit phone calls, TV broadcasts, computer data, and messages to satellites and submarines. They also store and read information on optical discs, bar codes and credit cards, and are used in printing books, newspapers and magazines. These two pages look at how lasers can do these things.

Satellite signals

Laser beams going straight through the air are not practical communications links, as they are badly affected by clouds and fog. However, they are important for sending signals to and between satellites in space, where there is no weather. A laser beam is almost impossible to intercept and so they are very important to military users.

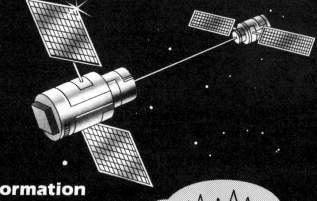

How beams carry information

In order to be stored or transmitted, all information – sounds, text, pictures or computer data – is turned into an electrical signal. This signal is an electrical form of the original, a microphone turns the varying sounds of your voice into a varying current of electricity which can travel along wires or be recorded. If a laser is stimulated by this electrical signal, it produces a beam that varies in the same way as the signal, and so in intensity in the same way as the original information. The beam can be used to carry the information, or store it on laser readable optical discs.

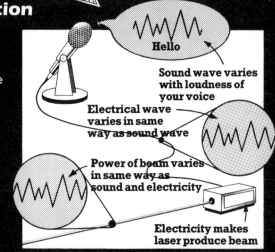

Hello

Sound wave varies with loudness of your voice

Electrical wave varies in same way as sound wave

Power of beam varies in same way as sound and electricity

Electricity makes laser produce beam

Optical fibres

Using light to carry information only became practical with the invention of optical fibres. These are flexible glass rods, as thin as hair, which act as "wires" for light. They work by totally reflecting the light inside so that none of it leaks out. Optical fibres are smaller than ordinary wires, yet light can carry much more information than radio waves and electrical signals, and so can provide more phone lines and TV channels. Optical fibre phone lines cannot be bugged or tapped.

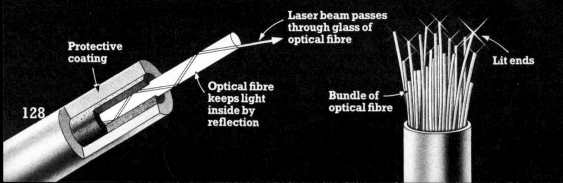

Laser beam passes through glass of optical fibre

Protective coating

Optical fibre keeps light inside by reflection

Bundle of optical fibre

Lit ends

128

Optical storage

The technology used for storing pictures and sounds on laser discs (see pages 114-115) can be used for other kinds of information too. Small, laser readable optical discs, like those shown here, may be widely used for storing computer data and software in the future. They are more hardwearing than the magnetic disks and tapes used now, and can hold more information.

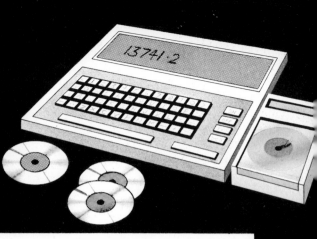

Laser printing

Lasers are being used for printing in several ways. This book was printed using sheets of metal, known as printing plates, with the words and pictures engraved on the surface. Lasers can be used to engrave the plates (see page 112). Printed type can also be produced with a technique very similar to this laser engraving. The beam is controlled in the same way to make letters, but instead of cutting a groove it is shone onto photographic paper. The laser exposes the paper and the places where the beam traced a path will become the dark marks of type when the paper is processed.

Another printing task for lasers is scanning or "reading" pages and turning the information into an electrical signal – (see bar codes below). This signal can then be transmitted to distant offices for printing.

Paper

Laser

Beam

Bar codes

Lasers are probably at work in your local supermarket or library, reading bar codes. A bar code is computerized information, encoded in a pattern of light and dark lines. A laser reads these lines by reflecting a beam off the pattern back to a detector in the "wand". The light and dark stripes make different reflections. The information is then decoded by computer. Bar codes can be used to store data of all kinds, from music to food prices.

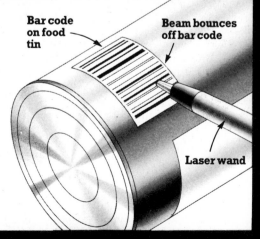

Bar code on food tin

Beam bounces off bar code

Laser wand

Measuring with lasers

Lasers are being used to help make maps, build skyscrapers and measure distances both huge and minute. The properties of laser light make it very useful for these jobs, which are explained on these pages.

Skyscraper

Laser beam is parallel and perfectly vertical

Laser plumb-line

As a laser beam is parallel and straight, even over large distances, it can be used as a kind of plumb-line or spirit-level to make sure that things are straight or level. The picture on the right shows a tall office block being aligned with a vertical laser beam during building. The beam's angle is monitored by special electronic equipment.

Laser tape measures

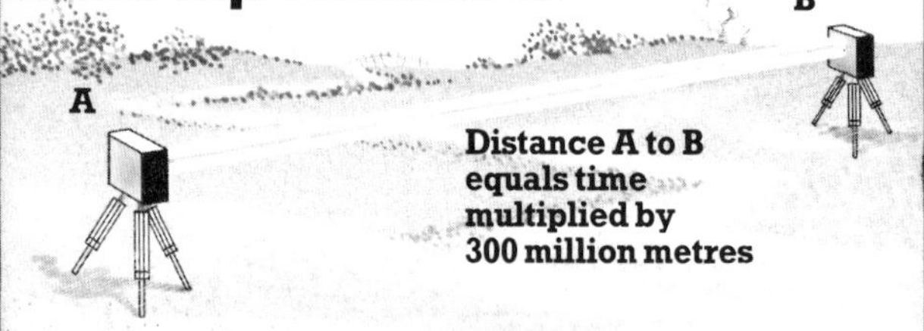

B

A

Distance A to B equals time multiplied by 300 million metres

A laser produces a beam of light and all light travels at a constant speed of 300 million m/s, in the air. So, a distance can be measured accurately by timing the passage of a laser beam between two places. The beam is timed with precise electronic equipment which also works out the correct distance.

Laser to the Moon

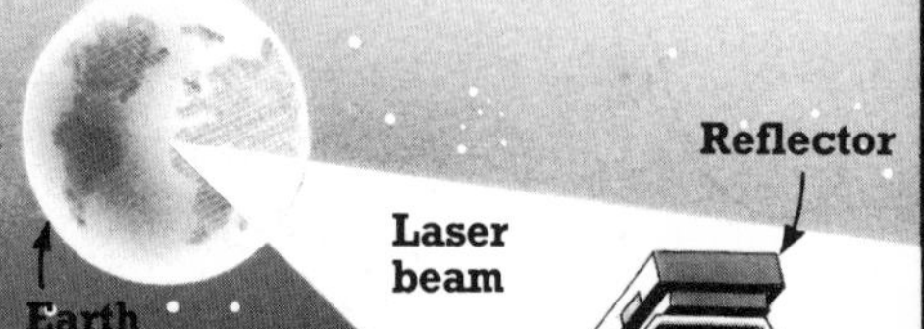

Reflector

Laser beam

Earth

The distance between the Earth and Moon has been measured by a laser beam, bounced back to Earth from a reflector left on the Moon. Although laser light is parallel over shorter distances, the beam spreads to about a kilometre wide over this vast distance.

Mapping the sea-bed

← Laser beam

Green light lasers are used to measure the depth of water and map the sea-bed. Light of this wavelength can penetrate water to a depth of several hundred metres. The laser is carried by a helicopter flying just above the surface. The beam bounces back to electronic timing devices.

Aligning pipes

Beneath our cities, countryside and seas are networks of pipes which carry essential services such as oil, gas, water, sewerage and communications cables for TV and phones. Engineers use the straight beams of lasers to help accurately lay and align these pipes. This picture shows one being used in a drainage sewer.

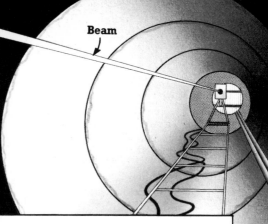

Beam

Microscopic measurements

An important property of a laser beam is that it is light of just one wavelength. Minute measurements are made by counting the number of wavelengths between one point and another. This is done with an "interferometer".

The interferometer works by splitting a laser beam in two, reflecting each part onto a different mirror and then recombining them into one beam. The two parts of the recombined beam will be out of phase, unless the difference between them is an exact whole number of wavelengths. This means that if one mirror is moved, a pattern of light and dark interference fringes is produced (see pages 120-121). A detector in the interferometer counts these fringes to work out the difference between the two beams, and therefore the distance by multiplying the number of fringes by the wavelength.

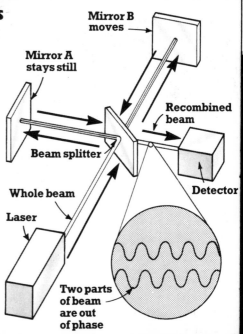

Mirror B moves

Mirror A stays still

Recombined beam

Beam splitter

Detector

Whole beam

Laser

Two parts of beam are out of phase

Sky heights

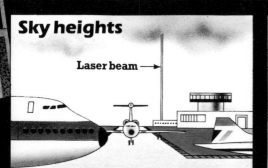

Laser beam →

Cloud height can be difficult to measure, especially at night, but it is very important to aircraft pilots. Some light wavelengths are reflected particularly well by the water droplets in clouds and lasers are now used at some airports in foggy or cloudy weather.

Reflective satellite

Corner-cubes

LAGEOS satellite

This satellite, called LAGEOS, reflects laser beams back to Earth. It is covered with special lenses, called corner-cubes, which send beams back to exactly where they came from. It is used to study tiny movements in the Earth's crust and the slow drift of the continents.

Laser weapons

When the laser was first invented, it appeared in science fiction as a deadly weapon. Many films still show "laser" swords, ray-guns and space cannons in action. So far, laser weapons are still mostly fiction, despite the fact that beams can be dangerous. Secret research is being carried out in several countries to make lasers that will destroy planes, missiles and satellites. The problem with this is that such lasers would have to be very powerful and extremely large – so not easy to manoeuvre or use. However, lasers are being used by the military in several ways other than as deadly rays, as shown on these pages.

Airborne laser lab

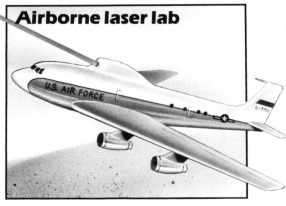

This is a picture of one of the few real laser weapons, built by the USA. It is a converted airliner housing a giant carbon dioxide laser. In tests in 1983 it shot down five missiles.

Shooting in the dark

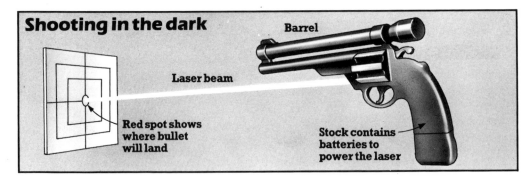

Barrel

Laser beam

Red spot shows where bullet will land

Stock contains batteries to power the laser

This ordinary looking hand gun has a helium neon laser mounted under the barrel. A slight touch on the trigger activates the laser and throws a spot of red laser light on the target. The spot is visible in the dark but it also helps with taking aim in daylight as the bullet lands exactly where the spot is. So the gun can be fired accurately "from the hip".

Range finding binoculars

These binoculars are mounted on an anti-tank gun and use a laser to measure the distance between it and a target. The soldier focuses the binoculars on the tank and sets off the laser. An invisible beam hits the target and bounces back into the binoculars where an electronic timer calculates how far away the target is (see pages 130-131 for more on this). The distance is shown in one of the eyepieces. If the tank is within range the soldier knows that by keeping it lined up through the binoculars he will make a direct hit.

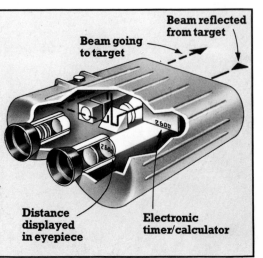

Beam reflected from target

Beam going to target

Distance displayed in eyepiece

Electronic timer/calculator

132

Laser guidance

Scattered light

Laser beam

Hunter-killer satellites

Missiles can be guided by laser beam to hit a target. A hidden soldier shines a laser beam onto the target, so that the light hits it and is scattered. The missile has a detector in its nose that picks up and homes in on this scattered light.

As laser beams can travel through space easily, they are being considered as space weapons. It may be possible to equip surveillance satellites with lasers so that enemy missiles could be destroyed from space when first spotted.

War "games"

Perhaps the strangest use of lasers is in the full-scale mock battles that armies carry out as practice for possible future war. The commanders want everything to be as realistic as possible, without using dangerous live ammunition. So they use laser "bullets" instead.

Soldiers have optical detectors all over their battledress and safe, low power lasers, like an aiming aid, fixed to their weapons. When a beam hits a detector an alarm is set off, so the soldier knows when he is "dead".

Laser beam

Laser fixed to gun barrel

Optical detectors

Video map displays shots and hits

Each "shot" and "hit" transmits a radio signal to computers which monitor the whole battle. The action is displayed on video maps for the commanders to see, rather like a complicated, real life computer game.

133

Lasers in chemistry

Many uses have been found for lasers in different areas of science, especially chemistry. They are used to detect and identify chemical elements and compounds, and to monitor and start reactions. The largest laser in the world is being used to try and develop cheap, safe, nuclear power.

Analysis by light

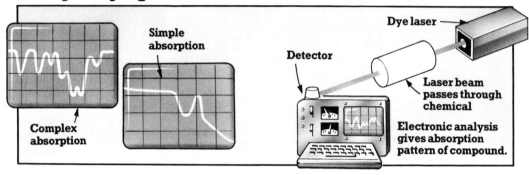

Simple absorption

Dye laser

Detector

Laser beam passes through chemical

Complex absorption

Electronic analysis gives absorption pattern of compound.

Chemists can find out a lot about chemical compounds by studying how they absorb different wavelengths of light. The chemicals in a substance can be identified by looking at the pattern of light absorption.

Some compounds have little absorption, in others the absorption pattern is complex. Analysis by light is called spectroscopy and a tunable dye laser is often used, as it can produce many wavelengths.

Chemical reactions

The energy of a laser beam can cause chemical changes in the substance that absorbs the light. The compound may be broken up into different chemicals and this process can be used to purify compounds. By tuning the laser to a wavelength absorbed by just one of the chemicals, the beam separates only those atoms or molecules, without harming the others.

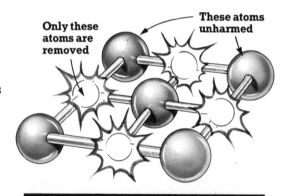

Only these atoms are removed

These atoms unharmed

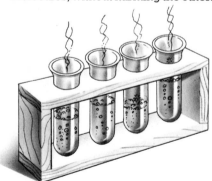

High power lasers can also be used to set off chemical reactions. They do this by breaking up the molecules with an intense flash of light. Once the reaction has begun, it carries on alone.

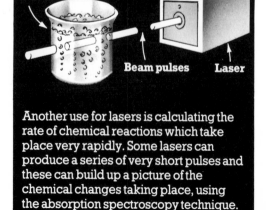

Chemical reaction

Beam pulses

Laser

Another use for lasers is calculating the rate of chemical reactions which take place very rapidly. Some lasers can produce a series of very short pulses and these can build up a picture of the chemical changes taking place, using the absorption spectroscopy technique.

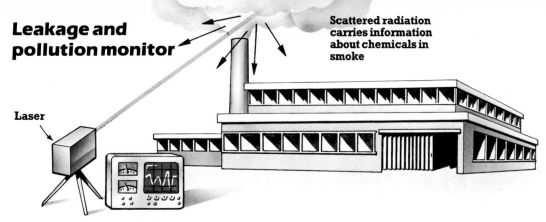

Scattered radiation carries information about chemicals in smoke

Laser

Laser spectroscopy can be helpful in looking for pollution and leaks of dangerous chemicals. This picture shows laser analysis of a plume of smoke from a factory chimney, checking for dangerous levels of poisonous pollutants. Laser detectors are very sensitive and can detect minute amounts of pollutant – levels of less than one part per million. They can run continuously and be connected to an alarm system.

Laser nuclear fusion

The ultimate chemical reaction is changing one element into another. Medieval alchemists tried to turn ordinary metals into gold, but failed. This "transmutation" does take place now, in nuclear reactions. The Sun is such a reactor as it fuses hydrogen into helium, producing energy which reaches us as light and heat. The same process causes the destructive energy of the hydrogen bomb. It requires enormous pressures and vast temperatures.

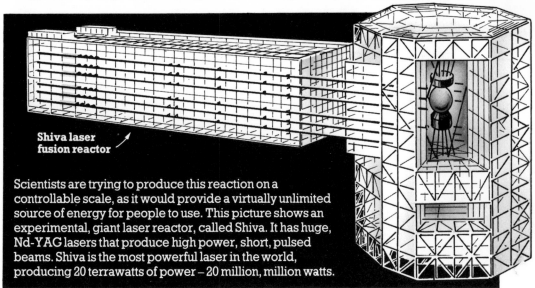

Shiva laser fusion reactor

Scientists are trying to produce this reaction on a controllable scale, as it would provide a virtually unlimited source of energy for people to use. This picture shows an experimental, giant laser reactor, called Shiva. It has huge, Nd-YAG lasers that produce high power, short, pulsed beams. Shiva is the most powerful laser in the world, producing 20 terrawatts of power – 20 million, million watts.

Outer layers of hydrogen heat and expand   **Inner layers are compressed**

Pellets of hydrogen are bombarded by these pulsed beams. The outer layers heat up very rapidly and expand, the inner layers of hydrogen are compressed. This should lead to nuclear fusion and production of energy. Shiva is just one experiment towards fusion and there is a long way to go before your home will be heated and lit by power from lasers.

Computing with lasers

Light travels faster than anything in the universe and scientists are trying to use the speed of laser beams to build faster computers. These two pages explain the research being carried out to apply lasers to the basic workings of the computer. Don't worry if you find this difficult to follow, it is very new research and unlikely to be in use until the next century.

How computers work

Computers are information processors which work by turning all information into a very simple code. This code is made up of just two signals – on and off – which can be written down as 1 and 0. It is called a binary digital code. Within the computer the code is actually produced by electonic switches, called transistors, which are either on or off.

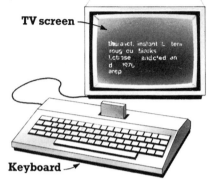

TV screen

Keyboard

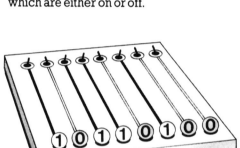

Since their invention almost 40 years ago, transistors have increased in switching speed and at present the fastest takes a nanosecond (thousand millionth of a second) to complete each switching operation. A switch which worked with light, instead of electronically, could be a 1000 times faster, switching every picosecond.

Optical "transistors"

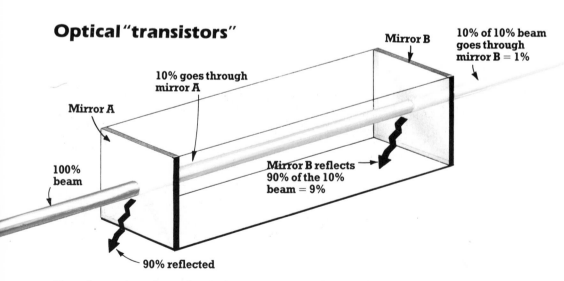

Mirror B

10% of 10% beam goes through mirror B = 1%

10% goes through mirror A

Mirror A

100% beam

Mirror B reflects 90% of the 10% beam = 9%

90% reflected

Experimental versions of optical transistors, called transphasors, have already been developed. They use the principle of interference to do the switching and so need laser light to work.

A transphasor is made of two mirrors with a space called the cavity in between. Both mirrors are partially silvered so that they reflect 90% of the laser beam and let through (transmit) 10% of it, as shown here.

How transphasors work

As laser light is coherent, interference takes place between the light waves going into the cavity through mirror A and those reflected by mirror B. If the two sets of light waves are out of phase, they will cancel each other out (destructive interference). If they are in phase they will reinforce each other (constructive interference). The kind of interference depends upon the distance between the mirrors.

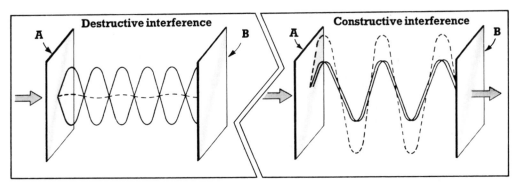

When there is destructive interference in the cavity almost no light gets through mirror B, because the light waves are cancelling each other out. The transphasor is switched off.

When there is constructive interference the light waves build up within the cavity and mirror B lets through a beam almost as bright as the original. The transphasor is switched on.

Optical switching

The next step is to switch the transphasor between on and off. This was done by using the ability of some materials to slow down the passage of light. Making the light travel slower has the same effect as moving the mirrors. Light travels at a constant 300 million m/s in a vacuum and in the air, but various materials, such as water and glass, slow it down. The cavity of the transphasor is filled with a special material which doesn't just slow the light, but slows it according to brightness. The brighter the beam, the slower it goes.

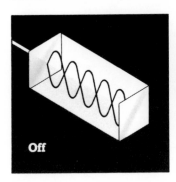

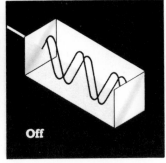

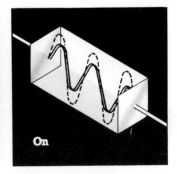

These pictures above show how an optical switching is done. The transphasor is off, as the mirrors are set for destructive interference.

As the brightness of the beam is increased, the material in the cavity slows the light. This changes the interference towards constructive.

If the intensity of the light continues to increase, the point of constructive interference is reached and the transphasor switches on.

137

Lasers at work

When the laser was first invented about 25 years ago, there were few obvious uses for it. Since then, however, an amazing range of things have been found for it to do. You probably have lots of things at home that were produced with the help of lasers in some way, although it is unlikely to be obvious – clothes, furniture, sunglasses, newspapers, electronic equipment, to name just a few.

Lasers fit into modern, high-tech industry because they are precise, accurate and controllable tools. They are very well suited for use with other new machines like robots and computers. The next four pages show more of the jobs lasers do, or are planned for them.

Road scanner

Beams bounce off road surface

This van scans the road as it travels by bouncing laser beams off the surface. The resulting measurements are analysed by a microprocessor on board, to provide data on the state of the road.

The Daily Laser

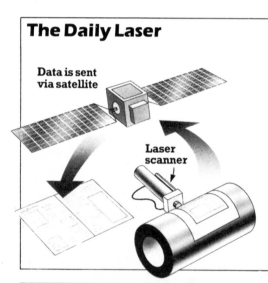

Data is sent via satellite

Laser scanner

The newspaper *USA Today* is a daily which covers the whole of the country. This is only possible using new technology, like lasers and satellites, as the USA is too large for country-wide distribution using ordinary methods. Laser scanners turn the words and pictures of each page into computerized data. This is then sent, via satellite, to newspaper printers all over the country, in a matter of seconds. At the receiving offices lasers are used to reconstruct and print the pages, so a single edition goes out all over the country at the same time.

Laser sight test

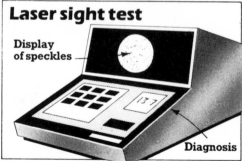

Display of speckles

Diagnosis

This machine uses the speckled coherence of laser light to test eyesight. If you have defective vision the speckles move – up for long sight, down for short sight. The speed shows how bad your eyesight is.

Shuttle docking

Shuttle's cargo bay open

Laser beam

Lasers will help Shuttle recover satellites on repair missions. Reflective pads on the satellite bounce the beam back, giving Shuttle's computers precise measurements so it can steer the craft to the satellite.

Gem security

MN 05735 700

Characters only visible with microscope

This picture shows a magnified view of part of a diamond. The microscopically tiny characters were engraved by laser onto the edge of the gem as an identification code to aid recovery if the diamond is stolen.

Unclogging arteries

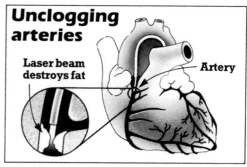

Laser beam destroys fat

Artery

Heart disease is often caused by fatty deposits in arteries of the heart. Tests show that lasers, delivered by optical fibres, could be used to vaporize this fat and unclog arteries.

Gas sniffer

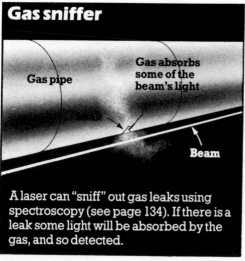

Gas absorbs some of the beam's light

Gas pipe

Beam

A laser can "sniff" out gas leaks using spectroscopy (see page 134). If there is a leak some light will be absorbed by the gas, and so detected.

Laser money

Bank of England £50 notes have a laser engraved pattern on the strip of silver embedded inside the note. Forgers will find this impossible to copy.

Eye drill

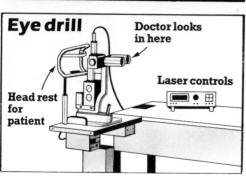

Doctor looks in here

Laser controls

Head rest for patient

Some eye problems are caused by a build up of pressure inside the eyeball. This can be treated by drilling tiny holes, with a laser, in the eye's outer surface to release the tension.

Flight display

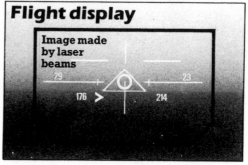

Image made by laser beams

29   23
176 >   214

This picture shows how lasers project an image of the controls of an aircraft onto the windscreen so that the pilot does not have to look down at them. It is called a Head Up Display (H.U.D.).

Fingerprint scanner

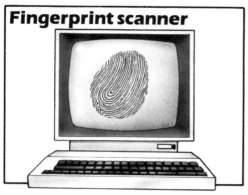

Everyone has unique fingerprints made up of whorls and ridges. They can be scanned by laser beam and the data stored on computer. This can be used by police, or even to enable your fingers to act as the key for a laser lock.

Laser wine taster

The taste of a wine depends upon the size of clumps of protein molecules that form within it – the smaller the clumps the tastier the wine. The quality of the wine can be measured by laser as the larger clumps scatter more light than the smaller ones.

Diamond holes

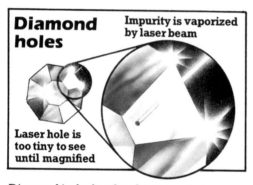

Impurity is vaporized by laser beam

Laser hole is too tiny to see until magnified

Diamond is the hardest known substance but it can be drilled by laser. Faults such as spots of carbon can be removed by drilling a tiny, invisible hole in the gem and vaporizing the black flecks.

Batting monitor

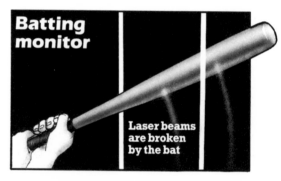

Laser beams are broken by the bat

Lasers are even used to time baseball batters' reactions and to monitor their batting power, speed and style. Two lasers make the measurements when the batter swings the bat through the beams.

Treating tumours

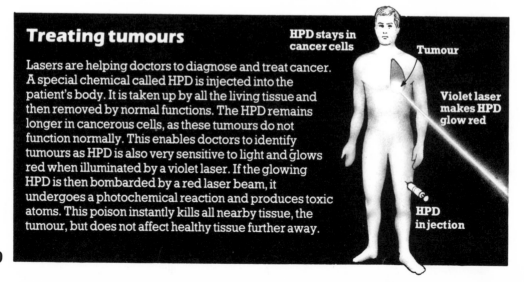

HPD stays in cancer cells

Tumour

Violet laser makes HPD glow red

HPD injection

Lasers are helping doctors to diagnose and treat cancer. A special chemical called HPD is injected into the patient's body. It is taken up by all the living tissue and then removed by normal functions. The HPD remains longer in cancerous cells, as these tumours do not function normally. This enables doctors to identify tumours as HPD is also very sensitive to light and glows red when illuminated by a violet laser. If the glowing HPD is then bombarded by a red laser beam, it undergoes a photochemical reaction and produces toxic atoms. This poison instantly kills all nearby tissue, the tumour, but does not affect healthy tissue further away.

Laser gun TV

A colour TV picture is made up of hundreds of horizontal lines formed from tiny glowing dots. In present TVs the spots are made by three electron guns; one each for red, blue and green. This system can only produce a picture on a special phosphor covered surface. In a new system lasers produce the red, green and blue beams which are combined to make the moving picture. The beams and spot are moved by a series of electronically controlled mirrors to create a picture. The image is much clearer than conventional TV and can be projected onto any surface.

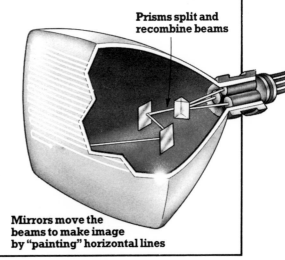

Prisms split and recombine beams

Mirrors move the beams to make image by "painting" horizontal lines

Light music

Laser beams

Photodetectors sends signals to synthesizer

This harp has laser beam "strings" which are played by passing your hand through the beams. The broken beams send signals to an electronic music synthesizer, which produces the notes.

Slow release medicine

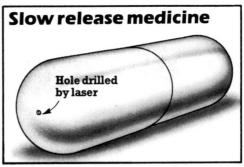

Hole drilled by laser

Many diseases need to be treated by an even level of drugs in the blood. This capsule has a tiny laser-drilled hole in its shell which releases a steady, constant dose of medicine.

Laser bug

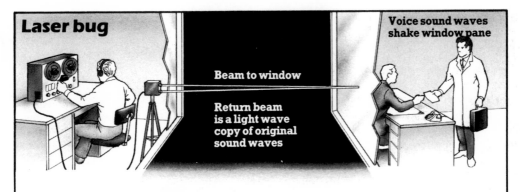

Voice sound waves shake window pane

Beam to window

Return beam is a light wave copy of original sound waves

A laser beam can be used to eavesdrop on a conversation, by bouncing the beam off the window of a room where people are talking. Their voices make tiny vibrations in the window pane. These would be picked up by the laser beam and carried back to a detector which turns the vibrations back into sounds.

Laser words

Argon: An inert gas used for filling fluorescent lamps and light bulbs. When excited, it produces laser action at green, blue and ultra-violet wavelengths.

Carbon dioxide: A gas produced by the burning of carbon compounds in air. When suitably excited by an electric current, it produces laser action as a long infra-red wavelength. When mixed with nitrogen and helium the laser output is increased.

Coherent: Describes electromagnetic radiation that has a single phase. The waves are all in step with one another, that is their peaks and troughs coincide with each other. Lasers produce coherent light but sources such as light bulbs and fluorescent tubes do not.

Electromagnetic radiation: Waves of energy with wavelengths varying from less than a million millionth of a metre to more than ten thousand metres and including all kinds of light, radio waves and X-rays. All electromagnetic radiation travels at 300 million metres per second in air.

Excitation: The process of increasing the energy of atoms or molecules into higher energy states. In lasers, this can be done, for example, by illuminating solids with light or by passing an electric current through gases.

Focus: The spot to which rays of light are converged by lenses or mirrors. With laser light, the size of the focused spot depends on the wavelength of the laser. Visible and near infra-red laser beams can be focused to about 2 or 3 micrometres, while carbon dioxide lasers are limited to about 50 micrometres.

Frequency: The number of complete waves produced in a second by a source. For electromagnetic waves, the frequency is obtained by dividing the velocity by the wavelength.

Fusion: A nuclear reaction in which one or more light elements join together to make a heavier one. In the Sun, hydrogen is being continuously fused into helium. This reaction, which also takes place in the hydrogen bomb, releases a large amount of energy. It can only take place at very high temperatures and intense pressure.

Helium neon: Two inert gases which, when mixed together and excited electrically, produce laser action. Helium neon lasers produce both visible and infra-red light but are used mostly as simple, comparatively cheap, red laser sources for alignment, etc.

Hologram: A three-dimensional recording of an image on photographic film or a photographic plate, using a laser light source.

Interference: Effect caused when two or more waves overlap. If peaks from two equal waves coincide, a bigger wave is produced (constructive interference) but when a peak coincides with a trough there is cancellation and the wave disappears (destructive interference).

Interference pattern (interferogram): The pattern produced by interfering waves. For two equal waves the pattern will vary from double size peaks to zero.

Interferometer: An instrument designed to produce interference effects. Interferometers can be used to measure the wavelength of light or, when used with a particular wavelength, to measure small distances very accurately.

Laser: The acronym (first letter of each word) of the phrase which describes the working of the device – Light Amplification by Stimulated Emission of Radiation.

Lens: A device, usually made of glass or quartz, for converging (focusing) or diverging a beam of light. Convex lenses converge and concave lenses diverge light.

Light: Historically used to describe electromagnetic radiation that is visible to the eye. Now it includes ultra-violet and infra-red wavelengths. Light that can be seen is called visible light.

Nd-glass, Nd-YAG: Neodymium has a set of energy levels suitable for laser action. Neodymium is put into a suitable material which transmits the laser light. YAG (yttrium aluminium garnet) and glass are the most common host materials.

Optical fibre: A very thin strand of glass or plastic which can carry light. Glass fibres are quite flexible and will transmit an infra-red laser signal over more than 100 kilometres.

Prism: A triangular shaped block, normally of glass or quartz for visible light, which bends (refracts) different colours at different angles. When white light falls on a prism it is separated into a spectrum.

Ruby: A form of aluminium oxide containing chromium. Chromium has a set of energy levels suitable for laser action.

Spectroscopy: The analysis of solid liquids and gases by studying their absorption and transmission of electromagnetic radiation of different wavelengths. Tunable lasers are particularly useful for this type of analysis.

Spectrum: Normally used to describe the range of colours that make up visible light. It is also often used to describe the whole range of electromagnetic radiation, when it is called the electromagnetic spectrum.

Transphasor: A term used to describe the optical equivalent of a transistor. In a computer, the electrical output of a transistor can be switched by an electrical pulse. In an optical computer, the light output of a transphasor can be switched by a pulse of light.

Wavelength: The distance between successive peaks of a wave. For example, green light has a wavelength of 500 nanometres.

White light: Light that is made up of all the visible wavelengths and appears white to the human eye.

Abbreviations

Ar	argon
Au	gold
CO	carbon monoxide
CO_2	carbon dioxide
Cu	copper
CW	continuous wave
HAZ	heat affected zone
HBr	hydrogen bromide
HCN	hydrogen cyanide
HeCd	helium cadmium
HeNe	helium neon
HF	hydrogen fluoride
I-R	infra-red
Kr	krypton
KrF	krypton fluoride
m/s	metres per second
N_2	nitrogen
Nd-glass	neodymium in glass
Nd-YAG	neodymium-yag
U-V	ultra-violet
YAG	yttrium aluminium garnet

Measurements

micrometre	millionth of a metre
nanometre	thousand millionth of a metre
millisecond	thousandth of a second
microsecond	millionth of a second
nanosecond	thousandth millionth of a second
picosecond	million millionth of a second
kilowatt	thousand watts
megawatt	million watts
gigawatt	thousand million watts
terrawatt	million million watts

Going further

Here are some of the galleries that have permanent exhibitions of holograms. You may find that your local museum or art gallery has visiting displays and there may even be shops selling small holograms and holographic jewellery.

Light Fantastic Gallery of Holography
48 South Row
The Market
Covent Garden
London WC2

National Museum of Film, Photography
  and Television
Bradford
West Yorkshire

Northern Light Fantastic
Edinburgh Wax Museum
142 High Street
Edinburgh

ZAP
45 Barlow Moor Road
Didsbury
Manchester

Holos Gallery
1792 Haight Street
San Francisco

Museum of Holography
11 Mercer Street
New York

143

Index

absorption, 107, 134
amplification 102, 103
argon (Ar) gas laser, 104, 116, 117

bar codes, 129
beam, laser, 100, 104, 106, 107, 109
beam splitter, 120
binary digital code, 136
binoculars, range finding, 132
bloodless surgery, 116, 117
bugging by laser, 141

carbon dioxide (Co₂) laser, 104,
  106, 112
  weapon, 132
carbon monoxide (CO) laser, 105
chemical lasers, 105
chemistry, laser use in, 135
coherent light, 101, 103, 121, 137
colour
  holographic, 119
  laser, 105
  mixing, 127
colours of the spectrum, 100
computers, use of, 111, 112, 126,
  136-137
constructive interference, 121, 137
continuous wave (CW) laser, 106
copper (Cu) vapour gas laser, 104
corner-cubes, 131
credit cards, hologram use in, 124,
  125
cutting by laser, 111

destructive interference, 121, 137
diamonds, faults in, 140
direction of light, 100
discs, laser, 115
drilling by laser, 108, 109, 110
dye lasers, 104, 107, 127, 134
electric current/signals, 102, 104,
  128
electronic control, 108
endoscope, 116
engraving by laser, 112, 129
excitation, 102, 103, 104, 105
eyesight testing, 138
eye surgery, 117, 139

flash tube, 105
flats, 114, 115
flight display, 139
focusing the beam, 108, 112
frequency, 100, 101

gas laser, 102-103, 104
gas sniffer, 139
gem security, 139
gold (Au) gas laser, 104
green light laser, 130

Head Up Display (H.U.D.), 139
Heat Affected Zone (HAZ), 111, 112
helium cadmium laser, 108
helium neon (HeNe) laser, 104, 114,
  116

holography table, 121
hydrogen bromide (HBr) laser, 105
hydrogen cyanide (HCN) laser, 105
hydrogen fluoride (HF) gas laser,
  105

image plane hologram, 123
incoherent light, 101
infra-red, 107
in phase, 101
interference pattern, 120-121, 125,
  131, 136, 137
interferometer, 131
inverted population, 104, 105

kerf, 111
krypton (Kr) laser, 104, 127

laser bullets, 133
laser readable optical discs, 129
laser weapons, 127, 132-133
lasing, 102, 103, 105
leakage monitoring, 135
light
  measurement of, 100
  patterns/shapes, 126-127
  reflection of, 118
light energy, 101, 102, 106
light waves, 100, 101

mapping the sea-bed, 130
measurement, 130, 131
medical lasers, 116, 117, 139, 140
miniature lasers, 104
mirrors, use of, 103
missile guidance, 133
monochromatic light, 100
movies, holographic, 122
multiple image, holographic, 122

neodymium in glass (Nd-glass)
  laser, 105
neodymium-yag (Nd-YAG) laser,
  105, 116, 135
normal state, 102
nuclear
  fusion, 135
  safety, 125

object beam, 120, 121, 122
one colour light, 99, 100, 103
one direction light, 103
optical fibres, 107, 116, 128
optical switching, 137
ordinary light, 99, 100
oxygen, use of, 109

paint stripping by laser, 109
parallax, 118, 119
peaks, 100, 101
photons, 101, 102
pipes, alignment of, 131
pits, 114, 115
plate, use in holography, 118, 119,
  120, 121
plumb-line, 130
pollution monitoring, 135
printing by laser, 129, 138
prism, use of, 100, 104

pseudoscopic image, 123
pulsed lasers, 106, 110

rainbow hologram, 119
real image hologram, 123
reconstruction, 119
reference beam, 120, 121, 122
reflection, 107
reflection hologram, 119, 122, 123
rhythm pulsing, 126
road scanner, 138
robot, industrial, 111

safety check by hologram, 125
satellite, 128, 131, 133
scanning by laser, 133, 138
semiconductor laser chip, 104, 113,
  114
shape cutter, 111
Shiva laser fusion reactor, 135
Shuttle, 138
skin treatment, 117
slow release medicine, 141
solid state laser, 105
speckle, 101, 138
spectroscopy, 134
spectrum, 100, 107
spontaneous emission, 102
spot
  power of, 108
  size, 108
spreading lens, 121
stimulated emission of radiation,
  102, 103
storage, optical, 114-115, 129
stress check by hologram, 125
surfaces, treatment of, 113
swarf, 110

tape measure, 130
tattoos, removal of, 117
teeth, treatment of, 117
telephone call by hologram, 124
three-dimensional (3D) image, 118
transistors, 136
transmission hologram, 119, 122,
  123
transmutation, 135
transparency, 107
transphasors, 136, 137
troughs, 100, 101
tunable lasers, 104, 107
TV, laser use in, 141

ultra-violet, 107

virtual image hologram, 123
visible light, 107

wand, laser, 129
war games, 133
watts, 106
wavelength, 100, 101, 104, 134
  energy of, 101
  laser, 107
welding by laser, 112, 113
  machine, 109
white light, 99, 100
whole image, 119

PRINTED IN BELGIUM